ONE THOUSAND

PROBLEMS IN PHYSICS

BY

WILLIAM H. SNYDER, A.M.

MASTER IN SCIENCE, WORCESTER ACADEMY, WORCESTER, MASS.

AND

IRVING O. PALMER, A.M.

MASTER IN NEWTON HIGH SCHOOL, NEWTON, MASS

BOSTON, U.S.A.

GINN & COMPANY, PUBLISHERS

The Athenæum Press

1900

PREFACE

—◦—

AN experience of some years in teaching physics in secondary schools has convinced the authors of the necessity of supplementing laboratory and lecture work with numerical problems.

The clarifying of pupils' ideas and the clenching of principles involved in laboratory exercises are believed to be materially furthered by the solution of suitable problems. The use of problems in physics gives also an opportunity for the review and practical application of the mathematics already studied.

Conversation with other teachers of physics has developed the fact that there is more or less widespread an opinion which coincides with that of the authors. The existence of this opinion and the need of a systematic collection of problems for our own classes furnish, in a measure, the *raison d'être* of this book.

Nearly all the problems have borne the test of class use and are, we believe, adapted to the needs of the secondary school pupil.

The collection has been made large in order that different problems may be used with different classes.

Through the courtesy of the Department of Physics of Harvard College the entrance examinations for the past ten years have been inserted.

The manuscript has been read by Mr. George W. Towne of the Classical and High School, Salem, Mass.

The proof sheets have been read by Prof. Albert de Forest Palmer of Brown University and Mr. A. B. Kimball of the High School, Springfield, Mass.

Mr. Frederick H. Holmes of the Normal School, Hyannis, Mass., has made many valuable suggestions.

To the above-mentioned gentlemen we beg to express our sincere thanks.

The authors only are responsible for any errors which may appear.

W. H. S.
I. O. P.

CONTENTS

———◦✦◦———

v

PROBLEMS IN PHYSICS

1. A uniform cylinder 20 cm. long and 10 cm. in diameter is filled with water. Will the average pressure per sq. cm. on the inside of the cylinder be greater when the cylinder is lying on its side, or standing on one of its ends?

2. Find the pressure per sq. cm. in mercury of density 13.6 at the depth of 65 cm.

3. Find the pressure at the depth of a mile in sea-water of density 1.026. (A mile equals 160,935 cm.)

4. A box 10 cm. square and 15 cm. long is placed with its longest side vertical, and has a tube extending through the top to a vertical height of 20 cm. Both the box and tube are filled with water. What is the pressure (*a*) on the top of the box? (*b*) on the bottom? (*c*) on one of the sides?

5. A cubical box 10 cm. on a side is filled with mercury. What is the pressure (*a*) on the top of the box? (*b*) on the bottom? (*c*) on one of the sides?

6. A cubical box 12 cm. on a side is filled with mercury. What is the entire pressure on the box?

7. In the previous problem, the box has a tube 1 cm. square extending through a hole in the top, and rising vertically 10 cm. above the top of the box. The tube is filled with water. What is now the entire pressure on the box?

8. There is a cubical box 20 cm. on a side filled with water. In the top of the box is inserted a tube 4 cm. square and 15 cm. long.   The tube is filled with oil of sp. gr. .75, which rests upon the water in the box.   What is the pressure (*a*) on the top of the box? (*b*) on the bottom? (*c*) on one of the sides?

9. Find the pressure per sq. cm. at the bottom of 2 cm. of mercury covered with 3 cm. of water and this again by 1.5 cm. of oil of density .9.

10. The cylinder of a pneumatic press is 2 ft. in diameter. What must be the diameter of the piston to multiply the pressure 400 fold?

11. A cubical block 20 cm. on a side is placed with its top at a depth of 100 m. in the sea.   What is the pressure on one of the sides?   Sp. gr. of sea-water is 1.03.

12. Find in cm. of mercury, atmospheric pressure being included, and the barometer standing at 76 cm., the pressure in water at the depth of 10 m.

13. At what depth in oil of density .9 is the pressure the same as in mercury at the depth of 10 cm.?

14. There is a closed box 20 cm. on a side.   Ten cm. down on one side a tube 1 cm. square enters and extends 10 cm. vertically higher than the top of the box.   The box and tube are filled with water.   Find the entire pressure on the six sides of the box.

15. A cubical box 10 cm. on a side is filled with mercury. In the top of the box is inserted a tube 1 cm. square, 10 cm. long and open at both ends, and filled with water. The water in the tube rests upon the mercury in the box. What is the pressure (*a*) on the bottom of the box? (*b*) on one of its sides?

16. If a cubical box be filled with water, prove that the entire pressure on the sides is 3 times the weight of the water.

17. A cylinder 3 ft. long and 2 ft. in diameter can withstand a uniform pressure on its sides of 500 lbs. to the sq. ft. If a tube 1 in. square is placed in the top, and the tube and cylinder are filled with water, (*a*) how long must the tube be in order that the pressure of the water may break the cylinder? (*b*) Where will it probably break? A cu. ft. of water weighs 62.5 lbs.

18. There is a tank 2 m. long, 1 m. wide, and 1 m. deep, having a pipe 4 cm. square and 2 m. long leading down from the center of the bottom. What is the pressure on the end of the pipe when the tank and pipe are filled with oil of sp. gr. .72 ?

19. What must be the size of a cubical box, so that if it is filled with a liquid of sp. gr. 5, the entire pressure on the bottom and sides shall be 960 g. ?

20. The area of the safety valve of an engine is 1 sq. in., and the weight upon it is 10 lbs. When the valve blows off steam, what is the pressure per sq. ft. on the boiler?

21. How long a tube must be inserted in the top of a cubical box 10 cm. on a side, so that when the tube and the box are filled with water the pressure may be the same on one of its vertical sides as it would be if the box alone were filled with mercury?

22. A cubical box 5 cm. on a side is filled with water. How long a vertical tube 1 cm. square must be inserted in the top and filled with water, in order that the pressure on one of the vertical sides may be just as great as the entire pressure on the box before the tube was inserted?

23. A pond 100 ft. wide and 20 ft. deep is kept in place by a dam sloping at an angle of 45° to the horizon. What is the pressure on the dam ?

24. A wedge-shaped vessel 5 cm. deep, the top of which is 6 by 4 cm. and the bottom 6 by 2 cm., is filled with water. What is the pressure on one of its larger sides?

25. The cistern of a barometer is placed 1 ft. under water. What will the barometer read if the atmospheric pressure is normal?

26. A dish 20 cm. in vertical height and shaped like the frustum of a square pyramid, 10 cm. on a side at one end and 15 cm. at the other, is filled with water and rests on its larger end. What will be the pressure on the bottom?

27. In the previous problem what will be the pressure on the bottom, if it rests on the smaller end? If there is any difference explain it.

28. A board 1 ft. square is sunk vertically in water, until the pressure upon its surface is 3125 lbs. What is the depth of its upper edge below the surface of the water?

29. A cubical box 5 cm. on a side is sunk in water until the top of the box is 10 cm. below the surface of the water. (*a*) What is the pressure on all the sides of the box? (*b*) If the box weighs 500 g., how much force is necessary to keep it submerged at this depth? In what direction must this force be exerted?

30. A cubical box 10 cm. on a side is filled ½ with water and ½ with oil (sp. gr. .6). If the two liquids take positions in accordance with their sp. grs., what will be the pressure (*a*) on the bottom? (*b*) on each of the sides of the box?

31. There is a vessel 15 cm. tall and 10 cm. square, which is filled with equal volumes of three liquids which do not mix. The sp. grs. are 2, 4, and 6. What is the pressure (*a*) on each side of the vessel? (*b*) on the bottom?

32. If in Problem 30 the oil and water are thoroughly mixed, what will be the pressure (*a*) on the bottom? (*b*) on each of the sides?

33. A cubical box 20 cm. on a side is filled with mercury and water half and half. What is the entire pressure on the box?

34. Suppose a tube 1 cm. square and 10 cm. long is inserted into the top of the box mentioned in the previous problem and filled with water, what will be the entire pressure?

35. Find in dynes per sq. cm. the pressure due to a depth of 1 cm. of mercury. Density of mercury equals 13.6.

DENSITY AND SPECIFIC GRAVITY

1. How would you find without the use of balances the weight of a wooden ball which, when placed in a tumbler full of water, causes an overflow of 100 c.c.?

2. A piece of aluminum weighs 200 g. in air and 100 g. in water. (*a*) What is its density in the French system? (*b*) in the English system? (*c*) its sp. gr. in the French system? (*d*) in the English system?

3. What will be the volume of 280 g. of substance of sp. gr. 14?

4. A given substance weighs 800 g. in air and 600 g. in water. What is (*a*) its volume? (*b*) its sp. gr.? (*c*) its density in the C. G. S. system?

5. What will be the weight (*a*) of a cu. ft. of iron of sp. gr. 7? (*b*) of a c.c.?

6. A block 7 × 7 × 3.5 cm. weighs 130 g. What is (*a*) its density? (*b*) its sp. gr.?

7. A piece of brimstone has a sp. gr. of 2.1. What will (*a*) 2 c.c. of it weigh? (*b*) 3 cu. ft.?

8. Eighty c.c. of a substance weighs 40 g. in water. What is its sp. gr.?

9. The weight of a given mass of substance is 660 g. ; its volume is 33 c.c.   What is its sp. gr.?

10. A certain volume of sulphuric acid of density 1.84 weighs 82.8 g.   The same volume of another liquid weighs 32 g.   What is the density of this liquid?

11. A cube of iron 10 cm. on a side weighs 7500 g. (*a*) What is its density?   (*b*) What will it weigh in alcohol of sp. gr. .92?

12. A cube 5 cm. on a side weighs 1.125 kg. in water. What is its sp. gr.?

13. A certain piece of brass loses 1250 g. in water. What is its weight?

14. How much will a kg. of iron weigh in sulphuric acid?

15. A rectangular block of stone measures 86 × 37 × 16 cm. and weighs 120 kg.   Find its density.

16. A cubical block of wood 15 cm. on a side weighs 1125 g.   What is its density?

17. What is the sp. gr. of a piece of gold that weighs 2000 g. in air and 1890 g. in water?

18. What will be the volume of a brass 500 g. weight?

19. What is the volume of a block of platinum which weighs 41 g. in water?

20. What is the volume of a piece of metal which loses 40.36 g. in nitric acid?

21. What is the volume of a piece of platinum that weighs 650 g. in milk of sp. gr. 1.03?

22. Find the volume of a solid which weighs 20 g. in air and 15.65 g. in oil of turpentine.

23. A body weighs 540 g. in air and 240 g. in a liquid twice as dense as water.   What is (*a*) the volume of the body? (*b*) the density?

24. What is the weight of a piece of metal of sp. gr. 8.9 that loses 51.1 g. in ether?

25. How much will a cu. ft. of lead weigh in oil of turpentine?

26. What is the weight (*a*) in air and (*b*) in alcohol of a copper rod 1 m. long and 2 cm. in diameter?

27. A block of tin weighs 347.5 g. What must be the sp. gr. of a liquid in which it will weigh 288 g.?

28. A piece of metal whose sp. gr. is 8 loses 224 g. in water. What is its (*a*) weight? (*b*) volume?

29. A piece of brass loses 25 g. in water. What will it weigh in sea-water of sp. gr. 1.026?

30. What will be the weight in ether of a cubical block 4 cm. on a side and of sp. gr. 1?

31. What will be the weight of a cubical block of iron 10 cm. on a side (*a*) in water? (*b*) in air? (*c*) in sulphuric acid?

32. A body weighs 30 g. in air and 27 g. in water. What will it weigh in mercury?

33. What is the sp. gr. of a body which weighs 1200 g. in water and 1260 g. in another liquid whose sp. gr. is .8?

34. What must be the sp. gr. of a liquid in which a cu. ft. of coal weighs 35 lbs.?

35. What must be the area of cross-section of a tube 10 cm. long which shall hold 20 g. of alcohol?

36. How many g. of alcohol will a tube 5 cm. long and 4 cm. in diameter hold?

37. A piece of platinum loses 25 g. in sulphuric acid. What is its weight in air?

38. In a certain liquid a piece of metal loses 25 g. In water it loses 30 g. (*a*) What is the volume of the metal? (*b*) What is the sp. gr. of the first liquid?

39. An iron rod is 12 in. long, 4 in. wide, and 2 in. thick. What is its weight (*a*) in water? (*b*) in air?

40. How much will a 100-lb. iron weight weigh in sulphuric acid of sp. gr. 1.8?

41. What is the weight of a zinc rod 2 m. long and 2 cm. in diameter (*a*) in air? (*b*) in ether?

42. A given bulk of lead weighs 250 g. How much will it weigh (*a*) in hydrochloric acid? (*b*) in kerosene?

43. What is the weight in copper sulphate solution of a mass of iron weighing 500 g. in air, if it loses 62.5 g. in water?

44. A certain substance of sp. gr. 12 weighs 60 g. in alcohol. What will be its weight in a liquid whose sp. gr. is 1.6?

45. A piece of zinc weighs 40 g. in sulphuric acid. What will it weigh in oil of sp. gr. .65?

46. How much will a brass kg. weight weigh in a liquid ¾ as heavy as water?

47. The loss of weight of a piece of brass in a liquid of sp. gr. 1¾ is 50 g. What is (*a*) its volume? (*b*) its weight in air? (*c*) its weight in water?

48. A piece of aluminum weighs 20.8 g. in air, 12.8 g. in water, and 15.28 g. in linseed oil. What is the sp. gr. (*a*) of the aluminum? (*b*) of the oil? (*c*) What is the volume of the aluminum?

49. How much does a cubical block of wood, 4 cm. on a side and of sp. gr. .5, weigh in water? What must be the sp. gr. of a liquid in which it will weigh 10 g.?

50. A piece of metal containing 8 cu. ft. weighs 3000 lbs. in water and 3100 lbs. in oil of turpentine of sp. gr. 0.8. What is (*a*) its sp. gr.? (*b*) its weight in air?

51. A body of sp. gr. 8.4 weighs 37 g. in water and 37.65 g. in oil of turpentine. What is the sp. gr. of the oil of turpentine ?

52. Find the density of a body which weighs 63 g. in air and 37.5 g. in a liquid of density .85.

53. A body of sp. gr. 6 weighs 25 g. in water, 26.35 g. in ether, and 24.81 g. in sea-water. Find the sp. gr. (*a*) of the ether ; (*b*) of the sea-water.

54. A certain volume of mercury weighs 216 g. and the same volume of another liquid weighs 14.8 g. Find the density of this liquid.

55. What is the sp. gr. of a liquid in which a body of sp. gr. 11 loses 50 g.? Its weight in water is 450 g.

56. A piece of metal weighs 20.4 g. in air, 14.4 g. in water, and 14.94 g. in linseed oil. What is the sp. gr. (*a*) of the metal ? (*b*) of the oil ? (*c*) What is the volume of the metal ?

57. A body of sp. gr. 2.5 weighs 31.25 lbs. in water. (*a*) What is its volume ? (*b*) What does it weigh in air ?

58. A lump of metal weighs a ton. Its weight in water is 1500 lbs. (*a*) What is its sp. gr. ? (*b*) What would be its weight in a liquid whose sp. gr. is 1.75 ?

59. A solid of sp. gr. 4 5 loses 40 g. when weighed in water. What is (*a*) its volume ? (*b*) its weight in water ?

60. The weight of a given solid is 500 g. ; its weight in water 450 g. ; and in nitric acid 439 g. What is the sp. gr. (*a*) of the solid ? (*b*) of the nitric acid ?

61. A given substance weighs 500 lbs. in air, loses 150 lbs. in water, and in a second liquid it weighs 240 lbs. What is the sp. gr. (*a*) of the substance? (*b*) of the second liquid ?

62. A block of stone of sp. gr. 3.4 weighs 337.5 lbs. in a liquid 3 times as dense as water, and 212.5 lbs. in another liquid. (*a*) What is the sp. gr. of the second fluid? (*b*) What is the volume of the block?

63. A diver with his suit on weighs 200 lbs. It takes $\frac{1}{35}$ of a cu. ft. of lead to just sink him. How many cu. ft. of water does he displace when in water?

64. A cube of pine 10 cm. on a side and of sp. gr. .5 has a hole 2 cm. in diameter and 5 cm. deep bored in the center of one face. The hole is filled with lead. How far will the cube sink in water?

65. A piece of silver when placed in alcohol is found to displace 9.6 g. When floated in mercury it displaces 9.25 c.c. What is (*a*) the weight of the silver? (*b*) the volume? (*c*) the sp. gr.?

66. A liter flask $\frac{9}{10}$ full of water just sinks in water. What is the volume of the glass composing the flask? The sp. gr. of glass is 2.5.

67. If a pint of water weighed exactly a pound, how many cu. in. would it contain?

68. A piece of wood containing 200 c.c. and of sp. gr. .5 is placed in a dish even full of water. (*a*) How much water will be displaced? (*b*) If it is placed in mercury, how many c.c. will be displaced?

69. The pressure of the air will hold water 30 ft. high in a vacuum. How high will it hold mercury?

70. What is the volume of a solid weighing 25 g. in air and 20 g. in water? If placed in a dish of mercury, what per cent of its volume will be submerged?

71. Find the volume of a solid which weighs 20 g. in air and 15.65 g. in oil of turpentine.

72. If the sp. gr. of air under ordinary conditions is .00129, and the sp. gr. of hydrogen .000105, what force will be needed to hold in place a balloon filled with hydrogen? The volume of the balloon is 125,000 c.c. and the weight of the balloon material is 100 g.

73. A body weighing 18 g. in air floats in water with ½ of its volume submerged. How many grams must be placed upon it to just submerge it?

74. A cubical block 2 cm. on a side floats ¼ submerged in a liquid of sp. gr. 1.2. How much water will it displace if floating in water?

75. A cubical block 10 cm. on a side floats ⅓ submerged in water. (a) What will be the sp. gr. of a liquid in which it floats with twice as much of its volume submerged as would be submerged in a liquid of sp. gr. 1.5? (b) What will be the volume submerged?

76. What is the sp. gr. of a liquid in which a solid will float with ½ as much of its volume submerged as would be submerged in alcohol of sp. gr. .8?

77. What proportional part of its volume will a wooden rod of sp. gr. .45 sink in alcohol?

78. To what depth will a block of stone of density 2.3 and cubical in form sink in mercury? Express your answer in terms of the edge of the cube.

79. If a body sinks ½ its volume in a liquid of sp. gr. .6, (a) what part of its volume will it sink in a liquid of sp. gr. .2? (b) What is the sp. gr. of the body?

80. A rod floats ½ submerged in alcohol. How much of the rod will be submerged in a liquid of sp. gr. .5?

· 81. A piece of cork floats on ether with 12 c.c. exposed. What is the entire volume of the cork?

82. A block weighing 40 g. in air floats in a liquid of sp. gr. .8 with ½ of its volume submerged. What is its cubical contents?

83. A uniform rod of sp. gr. .5 floats upright in alcohol with 10 cm. submerged. What is the length of the rod?

84. A rod 10 cm. long, composed of two substances whose sp. grs. are .5 and .9, respectively, floats ⅔ submerged in a liquid of sp. gr. 1.2. How much of each substance is in the rod?

85. There is a block of sp. gr. ⅔. How much of it will be submerged when floated on a liquid whose sp. gr. is 4?

86. How much will a cu. dcm. of copper project above mercury when floated upon it?

87. A stick of wood 20 cm. long and 2 cm. square, of sp. gr. .5, has attached to one end a piece of metal also 2 cm. square and 1 cm. thick of sp. gr. 5.5. How much of the length of the stick will be out of water when floated in it?

88. If a uniformly dense block of wood weighs 30 lbs. per cu. ft., (a) what is its sp. gr.? (b) What part of its volume will project above alcohol if floated upon it?

89. A rod floats ⅔ submerged in a liquid of sp. gr. .8. How much of it will be submerged in a liquid of sp. gr. .6?

90. A body weighs 12 g. in air and floats with ⅔ of its volume submerged in water. How many g. must be placed upon it to just submerge it?

91. There is a block 10 cm. on a side which sinks ⅔ of its volume in water and ½ in another liquid. (a) What is its sp. gr.? (b) What is the sp. gr. of the other liquid?

92. How many cu. ft. of wood of sp. gr. .4 will be required to float in water 500 lbs. of iron, if the iron is entirely submerged?

93. How many c.c. of cork must be attached to 10 c.c. of metal of sp. gr. 8, so that it will float in water entirely submerged?

94. How many grams of wood of sp. gr. .5 will a cubical block 10 cm. on a side, having a sp. gr. of 3.5, require to float it in alcohol when it is entirely submerged?

95. There is a uniform rod 6 ft. long and 4 in. square of sp. gr. .5. What must be the sp. gr. of a cube of metal 4 in. on a side, which when attached to the lower end, will submerge the rod in water?

96. There is a wooden rod of sp. gr. .5, 2 cm. square, and 20 cm. long, floating upright in water. How many c.c. of lead must be attached to the lower end to submerge ⅞ of the rod?

97. How many grams of lead must be attached to a cu. dcm. of cork in order that it may just float in linseed oil?

98. The sp. gr. of a certain metal is 7. How much cork will it take to keep 100 lbs. of this metal so that it will just float in the water?

99. There is a metallic cubical box 10 cm. on a side, outside measure, which weighs 500 g. The bottom and sides are ½ cm. thick. It is filled with sulphuric acid of sp. gr. 1.8. How much wood, sp. gr. .4, must be attached to this so that it will sink ½ its volume in water?

100. If the sp. gr. of pure milk is 1.03, and an inspected sample has a sp. gr. of 1.02, what per cent of the sample is water?

101. How many cu. ft. of lead must be attached to the lower side of 10 cu. ft. of wood of sp. gr. .4 to just sink it in a liquid of sp. gr. 1.2?

102. A cubical block 10 cm. on a side floats submerged ½ in a liquid of sp. gr. 1.2. How much lead must be attached to its lower side to just sink it?

103. How many c.c. of lead will a rod of wood 40 cm. long and 1 cm. square of sp. gr. .5 require to just submerge it when floating in alcohol?

104. A cubical block 10 cm. on a side floats ½ submerged in a liquid of sp. gr. 1.5. What must be the sp. gr. of a liquid in which it will float ¼ submerged after 10 c.c. of lead are attached to its lower side?

105. The sp. gr. of a certain stick 25 cm. long and 2 cm. square is .4. How much iron 2 cm. square attached to one end will it take to sink it in water so that only 2 cm. will be above the surface?

106. A rod 10 cm. long and 10 sq. cm. in area of cross-section, sp. gr. .3, has attached to one end an iron ball 1.4 cm. in diameter; when it is floated in brine, sp. gr. 1.3, how much of the rod will be above the brine?

107. What must be the sp. gr. of a liquid in order that a solid which sinks ⅓ its volume in ether may sink ⅔ of its volume?

108. What must be the sp. gr. of a liquid in which a body having a sp. gr. of 6.8 will float with ½ its volume submerged?

109. A body floats with ⅓ its bulk above water. What will be the sp. gr. of a liquid in which it will be half submerged?

110. What must be the sp. gr. of a liquid in which a solid which sinks ½ its volume in alcohol will sink ¼ of its volume?

111. A body floats ⅓ submerged in a liquid of sp. gr. .8 and ½ submerged in another liquid. What is the sp. gr. of the second liquid?

112. A rod 30 cm. long and 1 cm. square, composed ½ of hard wood and ½ of soft wood, sinks 21 cm. in water. The sp. gr. of the soft wood is .4.   What is the sp. gr. of the hard wood?

113. There is a rod 12 cm. long and 2 cm. square. Four cm. of length are of metal, the sp. gr. of which is 8, and the remainder of a metal whose sp. gr. is 10.   How far will this rod sink in mercury?

114. A rod 12 cm. long and 1 cm. square sinks 10 cm. in alcohol.   Half of its length is composed of wood of sp. gr. .3.   What is the sp. gr. of the other half?

115. If the density of brass is 8.5, what will be the weight in air of a mass of brass which weighs *in vacuo* 500 g.?   The weight of 1 liter of air is 1.2 g.

116. A flask which when filled with water weighs altogether 410 g. has 80 g. of a solid introduced, and being then filled with water weighs 470 g.   What is the volume of a kilogram of the solid?

117. A dish containing several weights sinks in salt water to a certain mark, and when placed in fresh water and 104 g. are taken out it sinks to the same mark.   What is the weight of both the dish and the weights left in it?   The sp. gr. of salt water is 1.026.

118. A wooden rod of sp. gr. .3, 30 cm. long, has attached to one end a spherical ball of metal 4 cm. in diameter and of sp. gr. 5.   What must be the area of cross-section of the rod so that just ½ of its length shall be submerged when immersed in water?

119. A cubical block of wood 2 cm. on a side weighs 5 g.   How far will it sink in alcohol of sp. gr. .8?

120. A body weighing 20 g. in air is attached to a sinker which weighs 30 g. in water.   Both together weigh 10 g. in water.   What is the sp. gr. of the body?

121. What is the sp. gr. of a liquid in which the body mentioned in the last problem will float with ⅔ of its volume submerged?

122. A solid lighter than water and weighing 25 g. in air is fastened to a piece of metal and both together weigh 36 g. in water. If the piece of metal weighs 45 g. in water, what is the sp. gr. of the light solid?

123. A body weighing 20 g. in air is attached to 2 c.c. of a metal of sp. gr. 11. They both together weigh 15 g. in water. What is the sp. gr. of the body?

124. The sp. gr. of a certain substance is 8. Ten c.c. of this substance are attached to a body which weighs 20 g. in air. Both together weigh 50 g. when submerged in water. What is the sp. gr. of the body?

125. A piece of wood weighs 8 g. in air, and when attached to a sinker which weighs 14.4 g. in turpentine they both, on being submerged in the turpentine, weigh 5 g. Find the sp. gr. of the wood.

126. A body weighs 20 g. in air and a sinker 30 g. in alcohol. They both weigh when submerged in alcohol 18 g. What is the sp. gr. of the body?

127. A body weighs 40 g. in air and a sinker 50 g. in a liquid of sp. gr. 1.4. They both together in this liquid weigh 20 g. Determine the volume and sp. gr. of the body.

128. A block weighing 10 g. in air and a sinker of sp. gr. 11 containing 2 c.c. are immersed in a liquid of sp. gr. 2. They weigh in this liquid 6 g. What is the sp. gr. of the block?

129. A liter flask weighs 25 g. When filled with a mixture of alcohol and water it weighs 867 g. How many c.c. of each in the flask?

130. A liter flask filled with mercury and water weighs 3570 g. (*a*) How much mercury in the flask? (*b*) How much water? The flask weighs 50 g.

131. A flask full of water weighs 500 g. When 120 g. of sand are put in and the water that overflows is allowed to run off, the flask is found to weigh 580 g. What is the sp. gr. of the sand? Disregard weight of flask.

132. There is a quart bottle half full of water and half full of another liquid. Liquids and bottle weigh 3 lbs. The bottle weighs ½ a lb. Find the sp. gr. of the second liquid.

133. A bottle when empty weighs 40 g., when full of mercury 543.2 g., and when 20 g. of mercury have been taken out and their place filled with another liquid it weighs 524.229 g. (*a*) What is the volume of the bottle? (*b*) What is the sp. gr. of the other liquid?

134. A bottle full of air weighs 625 g. When the air is partly exhausted it weighs 623.1 g. When the mouth is opened under water and the water allowed to take the place of the exhausted air, it weighs 2084.6 g. (*a*) What is the sp. gr. of the air? (*b*) How many c.c. of the air in the bottle were removed?

135. A certain vessel sinks to a mark in water, and after 10 g. are taken out it sinks to the same mark in a liquid of sp. gr. .6. What is the weight of the vessel and the contents?

136. A wooden vessel and load sinks to a certain mark in copper sulphate solution. On taking out 945 g. and placing in pure water it is found to sink to the same mark. What is the weight of both the vessel and the load it contained when in fresh water?

137. A weight of 25 g. is required to sink a Nicholson hydrometer to the mark. With a certain load on the pan it takes 17 g. to sink it. With the same load in the basket it takes 21 g. to sink it. What is the sp. gr. of the load?

138. It takes 45 g. to sink a Nicholson hydrometer to the mark. When a piece of quartz is placed upon the pan it takes 25 g. to sink it. When placed in the basket it takes 32.54 g. to sink it. What is the sp. gr. of the quartz?

139. A Fahrenheit hydrometer takes 62 g. to sink it to a certain mark on the stem when in water. It weighs 428 g. When placed in carbon di-sulphide it takes 140.4 g. to sink it to the same mark. What is the sp. gr. of the carbon di-sulphide?

140. A hydrometer sinks to a certain mark in a liquid of sp. gr. .6, but it takes 120 g. to sink it to the same mark in water. What is the weight of the hydrometer?

141. What volume of oak must be joined to 10 c.c. of flint glass in order that the sp. gr. of the whole may be 2?

142. Find the mean density of a substance composed of 8 parts by weight of a substance of density 4, and 12 parts of a substance of density 6.

143. Find the mean sp. gr. of a compound composed of 9 parts by volume of a substance of sp. gr. 7, and 6 parts of a substance of sp. gr. 3.

144. An alloy of gold and silver weighs 250 g. in air and 230.1 g. in water. (*a*) How much of it is gold? (*b*) How much silver?

145. The sp. gr. of two metals being 8 and 10, respectively, how much of each must be taken to make 100 g. of alloy having the sp. gr. of 9.4?

146. An alloy of gold and silver displaces 25 g. of water. An equal weight of silver displaces 35 g. (*a*) What is its volume? (*b*) How much gold is there? (*c*) how much silver?

147. A bar supposed to be pure gold on being tested was found to contain some copper. It weighed 402.3 g. in water and 426.8 in air. (*a*) How many c.c. of copper in it? (*b*) How many c.c. of gold?

148. To a piece of nickel is attached a piece of silver weighing 20 g. Both together weigh 30 g. in water. What is (*a*) the weight of the nickel? (*b*) the volume?

149. A liter flask is filled with a mixture of two liquids of sp. gr. 1.4 together. The sp. gr. of one of the liquids is .8 and of the other 1.8. What volume of each enters into the mixture?

150. Equal volumes of three liquids are mixed together. The sp. gr. of two of them are .8 and .9, respectively, and the sp. gr. of the mixture is 1.2. What is the sp. gr. of the other liquid?

151. Two liters of a liquid of sp. gr. 1.22 are mixed with 3 liters of a liquid of sp. gr. 1.8. The mixture shrinks to 4.6 liters. What is its sp. gr.?

152. How many c.c. of a liquid of sp. gr. 1.4 must be mixed with 1 liter of a liquid of sp. gr. .8 to make a mixture of sp. gr. 1.2?

153. A solid of sp. gr. 1.5 floats with ⅓ its volume submerged on a mixture of equal parts water and another liquid. What is the sp. gr. of the second liquid?

154. A bottle when empty weighs 20 g.; when full of nitric acid it weighs 66.8 g., and when full of olive oil 47.45 g. What is the sp. gr. of the olive oil?

155. A certain bottle when full of ether weighs 194 g. How much will it weigh when full of sulphuric acid? The weight of the bottle is 50 g.

156. What is the diameter of a spherical ball that can be made from a brass kg. weight?

157. Mercury is 13.6 as heavy as water. How much higher can water be raised in a perfect acting lifting pump on a day when the barometric pressure is 78 cm. than on a day when it is 74 cm ?

158. When the barometer stands at 760 mm. to what height can sulphuric acid of sp. gr. 1.8 be raised in a suction pump which is able to cause a barometer placed in a bell jar from which it exhausts the air to fall from 760 mm. to 20 mm. ?

159. A cylindrical rod 3.5 m. long weighs 12.5 kg. in air and 2 kg. in water. Find radius and sp. gr.

160. The weight of a liter of hydrogen at 0° C. and 760 mm. pressure is .0896 g. Nitrogen is 14 times as heavy and oxygen 16 times as heavy as hydrogen. Air is composed of a mixture of 4 parts nitrogen and 1 part oxygen. What is the weight of a liter of air at the same temperature and pressure ?

161. A *U*-tube is filled with water and glycerine unmixed. The height of the glycerine above the line of meeting is 70 cm. The height of the water on the other side of the tube above this line is 88.9 cm. What is the sp. gr. of the glycerine ?

162. Two liquids in the opposite arms of a *U*-tube stand at 50 and 60 cm., respectively, above their point of junction. The sp. gr. of the first liquid is .8. What is the sp. gr. of the second ?

163. Two vertical tubes have their upper ends connected by a *V*-tube and their lower ends in oil and sulphuric acid. The air is partly exhausted from the tube, and the oil is found to rise 80 cm. and the sulphuric acid 34.8. What is the sp. gr. of the oil ?

164. A brass wire 7 m. long weighs in air 184.36 g. and in water 162.36 g. What is (*a*) its volume? (*b*) sp. gr.? (*c*) radius?

165. There is a uniform glass tube 2 cm. in inside diameter and 20 cm. long. It weighs 50 g. From the center to one end it is filled with kerosene of sp. gr. .8, and the other end is filled with copper sulphate, of sp. gr. 1.2. Where will the rod balance?

166. A rod 20 cm. long and 1 cm. square has 5 cm. of its length composed of iron, 12 cm. of wood, of sp. gr. .5, and the remainder of lead. At what distance from the iron end is the center of gravity?

167. A ring containing a supposed diamond weighed 46.5 g. in air and 43.5 g. in water. The gold put into it weighed 45 g. The sp. gr. of the gold was 18 and the sp. gr. of a real diamond is 3.5. Was the stone a diamond?

168. A piece of silver weighing 20 g. and a piece of tin are fastened to the two ends of a string passing over a pulley and hang in equilibrium when immersed in water. Determine the weight of the tin.

169. Ten c.c. of silver are attached to one end of a string passing over a pulley. The silver is immersed in alcohol. How large a piece of brass attached to the other end of the string and immersed in water will just balance the silver?

170. A cube of platinum 2 cm. on a side attached to one arm of a balance is completely immersed in mercury. It is exactly counterbalanced by a sphere of lead attached to the other arm of the balance and completely immersed in water. What is the diameter of the sphere?

171. What will be the acceleration of a body of sp. gr. 5, when dropped into a liquid of sp. gr. 2? Neglect friction.

172. A liter flask filled with mercury weighs 14,000 g. When some of the mercury is poured out and water put in to take its place, the flask and contents weigh 12,740 g. (*a*) What is the weight of the flask? (*b*) How much water is put in?

173. A flask when filled with mercury weighs 4100 g. When ⅓ of the mercury is turned out and its place filled with a liquid of sp. gr. 1.6, it weighs 2900 g. Determine the weight and volume of the flask.

174. A cube of wood 10 cm. on a side, resting on the horizontal bottom of a dish, makes a perfectly tight contact but does not adhere. If water is poured on until the block is entirely covered, how much weight must be put upon the block to keep it from floating? The sp. gr. of the block is .5.

175. There is a rod 70 cm. long, 10 cm. square, of sp. gr. .5, that rests on the bottom of a vessel 50 cm. deep. What will be the tension on a string 10 cm. long, which is attached to the bottom of the vessel and to the lower end of the rod, when in the dish full of water?

176. A piece of wood of sp. gr. .4, 10 cm. long and 6 cm. square, is fastened to the bottom of a dish by a string attached to one end. If copper sulphate solution be poured in so as to cover the wood, what is the tension on the string?

177. A wooden sphere 10 cm. in diameter, and of sp. gr. .5, is attached by a string to the bottom of a dish and alcohol is poured on until the sphere is covered to a depth of 10 cm. What is the tension on the string?

178. A block floats in water with ½ its volume submerged. How much of its volume will be under water when a liquid of sp. gr. .25 is poured on so as to cover the entire block?

179. A block floats ½ submerged in a liquid of sp. gr. 1.2. How much of it will remain in the liquid after another liquid of sp. gr. .4 is poured on until the block is covered?

180. A body floats ⅔ submerged in a liquid of sp. gr. 1.8. What is the sp. gr. of a liquid which, if turned on so as to entirely cover the body, will cause it to float with ½ its volume in each liquid?

181. A cubical block 10 cm. on a side, and of sp. gr. .5, is floating in water. Oil of sp. gr. .3 is poured on to the depth of 2 cm. How much of the block is above the oil?

182. In the previous problem how much oil must be poured on to bring the surface of the oil just on a level with the upper surface of the block?

183. A marble 2 cm. in diameter floats on mercury with ¼ of its volume submerged. If oil of sp. gr. .8 be poured on until the marble is entirely covered, how much of it will be in mercury? How much additional pressure will it exert upon the bottom of the enclosing dish?

184. A liquid of sp. gr. .4 is poured upon a cubical block of wood 10 cm. on a side, floating ½ submerged in water, until the top of the block is just even with the top of the liquid. What is now the lateral pressure on each of the sides of the block?

TENACITY AND ELASTICITY.

1. How many times as much weight will a wire which is ⅓ as long and twice as thick as another of similar material support?

2. How much must the diameter of a wire be increased to treble its strength?

3. If No. 27 spring brass wire breaks with a pull of 15 lbs., what must be the diameter of a spring brass wire that will just sustain a load of 100 lbs?

4. How much load will No. 15 wire sustain if No. 27 sustains 15 lbs.?

5. If No. 25 spring brass wire breaks with a pull of 15 lbs., what is the breaking strength of No. 5? No. 9? No. 16? No. 21? No. 30?

6. Using the data of the previous problem, what is the diameter of a brass wire which will just sustain (*a*) a load of 100 lbs.? (*b*) a load of 50 lbs.?

7. If No. 27 brass wire breaks with a pull of 15 lbs., and No. 30 steel wire with a pull of 9 lbs., what is the relative tenacity of steel and brass?

8. Using the data of the previous problem, what is the diameter of the smallest brass wire that will not be broken by two boys each pulling against the other with a force of 100 lbs.?

9. If No. 25 spring brass wire breaks with a pull of 25 lbs., and No. 30 steel wire with a pull of 18 lbs., what is the relative tenacity of brass and steel?

10. What is the relative tenacity of brass and steel if No. 17 steel wire can sustain a load of 50 lbs.? [Use data from Problem 7.]

11. What is the relative tenacity of copper and steel if No. 32 copper wire just sustains a load of 2½ lbs.? [Data from Problem 7.]

12. What loads will (*a*) No. 12 brass wire sustain? (*b*) No. 12 steel? [Data from Problem 7.]

13. What size of steel wire would it be necessary to use in making the links of a chain which is to sustain a weight of 100 lbs.? [Data from Problem 7.]

14. A wire the diameter of which is 1.2 mm. breaks with a pull of 10 lbs., another, the diameter of which is .04 mm., with a pull of 2 lbs. What is the relative tenacity of the two wires?

15. A wire .4 mm. in diameter breaks with a force of 40 lbs.; another wire .5 mm. in diameter with a force of 50 lbs.   What is their relative tenacity?

16. No. 27 copper wire breaks with a pull of 15 lbs. If the tenacities of copper and iron are to each other as 3:2, find the breaking strength of No. 26 iron wire.

17. If the tenacities of silver and iron are to each other as 1:2, what will be the relative diameter of wires of these metals which sustain the same weights?

18. What must be the diameter of a brass wire in order that it may support the same weight as a platinum wire .8 mm. in diameter?   The tenacities of brass and platinum are as 3:1.

19. The tenacities of two wires are to each other as 3:2. A wire of the first kind .25 mm. in diameter breaks with a pull of 10 lbs.   How much pull will it take to break a wire of the second kind .35 mm. in diameter?

20. If the pull on a wire be doubled and its diameter trebled, how will its stretch be affected?

21. The pull on two wires being the same, what will be their relative stretches if one of them is twice as long and ½ as thick as the other?

22. If a wire 1 m. long and 1 mm. in diameter be stretched 1 mm. by a force of 3 lbs., how far will it be stretched by a force of 4 kg.?

23. A force of 3 lbs. stretches 1 mm. a wire that is 1 m. long and .1 mm. in diameter.   How much force will it take to stretch 5 mm. a wire of the same material 4 m. long and .15 mm. in diameter?

24. Using data in the previous problem, how much will a force of 10 lbs. stretch a wire 5 m. long and .5 mm. in diameter?

25. What will be the diameter of a wire 3 m. long that will stretch 4 mm. when pulled by a force of 8 lbs., if a wire 1 m. long and .1 mm. in diameter stretches 1 mm. when pulled by a force of 3 lbs.?

26. A piece of No. 18 wire 3 m. long is stretched 1 cm. by a certain force. How long a piece of No. 24 wire will be stretched twice as much by the same force?

27. How much greater pull must be exerted upon a piece of No. 20 brass wire 5 m. long than upon a piece of No. 27 wire 3 m. long, in order to stretch them the same . amount?

28. What is the ratio between the force necessary to stretch 5 m. of No. 24 wire .4 cm. and the force needed to stretch an equal length of No. 32 wire the same distance?

29. The lengths of two wires are to each other as 4:5 and their diameters as 3.2. What will be their relative amount of stretch under the same pull?

30. A piece of No. 17 and a piece of No. 26 iron wire stretch the same amount under the same pull. What are the relative lengths?

31. If a force of 2 lbs. stretches 2 mm. a wire which is 1 m. long and .1 sq. mm. in cross-section, how great a force is needed to stretch 5 mm. a wire of like material 10 m. long and 1 sq. mm. in cross-section?

32. A wire 4 m. long and .36 mm. in diameter is stretched 1 cm. by a pull of 5 lbs. How much will a wire 3 m. long and .25 mm. in diameter be stretched by a pull of 6 lbs.?

33. Using data in previous problem, how much pull will be necessary to stretch 4 cm. a wire 5 m. long and .4 mm. in diameter?

34. A wire 4 m. long and .1 mm. in diameter is stretched 8 cm. by a force of 5 lbs. What must be the length of a wire .2 mm. in diameter that will stretch 2 cm. when pulled by a force of 10 lbs.?

35. A wire 4 m. long and .2 mm. in diameter is stretched 4 cm. by a force of 5 lbs. What must be the length of a wire .3 mm. in diameter that it may be stretched 2 cm. by a force of 10 lbs.?

ROD OF RECTANGULAR CROSS-SECTION.

GIVEN PROBLEM	LENGTH, 100 CM	WIDTH, 1 CM	THICKNESS, 1 CM	LOAD, 100 G	DEFLECTION • 8 MM
36.	100	1	1	150	?
37.	100	1	$\frac{2}{3}$	100	?
38.	100	$1\frac{1}{3}$	1	100	?
39.	75	1	1	100	?
40.	100	1	1	?	20
41.	100	1	?	100	27
42.	100	?	1	100	10
43.	?	1	1	100	27
44.	100	?	1.2	100	8
45.	150	1	?	200	6.75
46.	40	4	1	2500	?
47.	350	$3\frac{1}{2}$	2	450	?
48.	100	?	$\frac{1}{2}$	100	1.6
49.	80	$\frac{1}{2}$	4	2000	?
50.	100	1	1.2	200	?
51.	200	4	$\frac{1}{2}$	?	36
52.	100	$\frac{2}{3}$	?	625	8
53.	125	$1\frac{1}{3}$	?	150	9
54.	225	?	$1\frac{1}{2}$	500	27
55.	75	4	?	800	16

56. A wire 4 m. long and 2 mm. in diameter is stretched 5 mm. by a force of 10 lbs. What is the diameter of a wire 2 m. long if it is stretched 6 mm. by a force of 8 lbs.?

57. A wire 5 m. long and .4 mm. in diameter is stretched 12 mm. by a force of 5 lbs. What must be the diameter of a wire 3 m. long to cause it to stretch 5 mm. under a pull of 2 lbs.?

58. If a wooden rod ½ in. square, fastened at one end, is twisted 5° by forces applied at the other end, how much would it have been twisted (*a*) by forces twice as great and similarly applied? (*b*) by forces 3 times? (*c*) 5 times? (*d*) 7 times? (*e*) ½ times? (*f*) ⅔ times? (*g*) 10 times as great?

59. How much would the forces of the last problem twist a rod (*a*) twice as long as that mentioned, but similar in other respects? (*b*) a rod 3 times as long? (*c*) ⅔ as long? (*d*) ½ as long?

60. How much would a rod 1 in. square, but in other respects like that of Problem 58, be twisted by the same forces mentioned in that problem?

61. Assuming that the torsional stiffness of spruce wood is twice that of pine, and that a spruce rod ½ in. square, firmly fastened at one end, is twisted 10° by certain forces applied at the other end, (*a*) how much will a pine rod, similar in other respects, but twice as long, be twisted by the same forces? (*b*) how much by forces ½ as great?

62. If a pine rod similar to that of Problem 61, but 1 in. square, were subjected to forces twice as great as those above mentioned, how much would it be twisted?

COMPOSITION AND RESOLUTION OF FORCES

1. What is the tension on a wire whose ends are attached, one to a hook in the ceiling of a room, the other to a 25-lb. weight which it supports?

2. Eight men are engaged in a tug of war which results in a draw. Each man exerts a force of 300 lbs. What is the tension on that part of the rope between the two teams?

3. Find the magnitude and position of the resultant of two parallel forces of 16 and 24 lbs., respectively. They act in the same direction and their points of application are 5 ft. apart.

4. Two forces of 6 and 8 units act upon a body in lines which meet in a point and are at right angles. Find the magnitude of their resultant.

5. Resolve a force of 500 kg. acting N.E. into two forces, one acting E. and the other N.

6. Resolve a force of 100 lbs. into two forces acting at right angles to each other, one of which shall be twice as great as the other.

7. Resolve a force of 50 g. into two forces at right angles to each other, one of which shall be three times as great as the other.

8. How great must be the force that can be resolved into two forces, the smaller of which, 50 lbs., acts N., and the larger, 80 lbs., acts E. In what direction must it act?

9. Two forces which are in the ratio of 2 : 3 act perpendicularly to each other upon a point and produce a resultant force of 26 lbs. Determine the value of these forces.

10. What force can be resolved into two components at right angles to each other, one of which shall be 20 and the other 60 lbs. ?

11. Resolve a force of 20 lbs. into two components acting at an angle of 60° with each other. [Plot.]

12. Resolve a force of 30 lbs. acting vertically into two components, one of which acts at an angle of 30° to the vertical and the other at an angle of 45° to the vertical.

13. There is a force of 1000 g. acting S. This is kept in equilibrium by two forces, one acting N.E. and the other W. Determine by plotting the magnitude of each force.

14. The force BA of 10 lbs. acts N. upon the point A. The force CA of 15 lbs. makes an angle of 30° with BA to the E., and DA of 20 lbs. makes an angle of 60° to the W. Find the resultant.

15. The wind is blowing to the S.W. with an actual velocity of 20 miles per hour. Find its southerly and westerly components.

16. Forces of 10 lbs. acting N.; of 5 lbs. acting N.E.; of 20 lbs. acting E.; and of 15 lbs. acting S.E impinge upon a body. (a) In what approximate direction will the body move? (b) By what resultant force is it acted upon?

17. A balloon rises 500 ft. per minute and at the same time is blown along by the wind at the rate of 300 ft. per minute. What is its rate of motion ?

18. At what angle can two equal forces act upon each other so that equilibrium is produced?

19. The resultant of two forces is 20. One of the forces is 12, and the other is inclined to it at an angle of 90°. What is the second force?

20. Two forces of 10 lbs. each act at an angle of 120° to each other. What is the resultant force ?

21. A railway car is moving at the rate of 30 miles per hour. A ball is moved directly across the car at the same rate. (*a*) How fast does the ball move relatively to the ground? (*b*) At what angle to the direction of motion of the car?

22. Two boys strike a football at the same instant, one with a force of 25 lbs. acting N., and the other with a force of 30 lbs. acting E. What direction will the ball take?

23. The southerly component of the wind is 10 miles per hour and the westerly component is 15 miles per hour. Find the direction and velocity of the wind.

24. A body is moved E. with a constant velocity of 40 ft. per second and N. with a constant velocity of 60 ft. per second. What is its actual rate of motion in a straight line?

25. A ship borne N. by the wind at the rate of 10 miles per hour strikes a current flowing N.E. at the rate of 6 miles per hour. (*a*) What direction will the ship take? (*b*) How far will it travel in one hour?

26. A boat is rowed at right angles to the course of a river twice as fast as the river flows. It makes the opposite shore 1½ miles below the starting point. What is the breadth of the river?

27. A man rowing a boat across a river 3 miles wide, at the rate of 4 miles per hour, is carried down by the current at the rate of 2.5 miles per hour. (*a*) How far from the starting place will he be when he reaches the other side? (*b*) How far below the place directly opposite the starting point?

28. A rod extending N. and S. has 2 cm. from the north end a force of 20 g. acting E.; 4 cm. from the north end a force of 15 g. acting W.; 6 cm. from the north end a force of 10 g. acting E.; and 8 cm. from the north end a force of 5 g. acting W. (*a*) Where must a force be applied to produce equilibrium? (*b*) How great must it be?

29. A weightless rod, *AB*, is 12 cm. long and has acting upon it 5 forces; one at end *A* of 10 g. acting down; one at end *B* of 6 g. acting down, 3 cm. from *A* a force of 16 g. acting up; 7 cm. from *A* a force of 12 g. acting up; and 2 cm. from *B* a force of 5 g. acting down. (*a*) What is the value of the equilibrating force? (*b*) How far from *B* must it be placed?

30. A board 3 ft. square is so placed that its sides extend in the directions of the four cardinal points of the compass. One ft. west of the east end of the north side a force of 10 lbs. acts north, and 1 ft. east of the west end of the south side a force of 10 lbs. acts south. (*a*) Where can two other forces be placed so as to keep the board in equilibrium? (*b*) How great must they be?

31. A board 2 ft. square so placed that its sides extend N., S., E., and W. has attached to the N.W. corner a force of 100 lbs. acting N., and from the center of the south side a force of the same amount acting south. (*a*) In what direction must forces act upon two of the corners to produce equilibrium? (*b*) Upon what corners must they act? (*c*) How great must they be?

32. A horse is attached to a sleigh so that the traces make an angle of 30° with the surface of the snow. Supposing the sleigh offers a resistance of 500 lbs. to horizontal motion, how much must the horse pull to move it?

33. There is a hill the surface of which is inclined at an angle of 45° to the horizon. A sled weighing 100 lbs. rests upon this. How much of the weight of the sled will tend to produce motion down the hill?

34. A sled weighing 50 lbs. rests on the side of a hill rising 1 ft. in 30 along the incline. What force acting parallel to the surface of the hill will keep the sled from sliding down the hill? Disregard friction.

35. A man drags a weight by a rope passing over his shoulder and making an angle of 45° with the surface of the ground. The tension on the rope is 75 lbs. If the friction is not considered, how much force acting parallel to the ground would it take to move the weight?

36. The horses attached to a car are pulling at an angle of 45° to the track with the force of 1 ton. (*a*) How much of this force is used in pulling the car along the track? (*b*) How much in pressing the wheels against the side of the track?

37. A pair of horses moving on a level against a force of 1800 lbs. pull at an angle of 90° to each other. One pulls ⅓ more than the other. How much does each pull?

38. Resolve the force 48 into two forces making angles of 45° with the given force on either side of it.

39. An inclined plane rises 1 ft. in 8 of horizontal distance. What force acting up the plane and parallel to it will just sustain a mass of 168 lbs. on the incline?

40. A body weighing 10 lbs. rests upon an inclined plane which rises 3 ft. in 4 of horizontal distance. What is the pressure vertical to the plane?

41. What must be the breaking strength of a board which, when inclined at an angle of 45° with the horizon, just sustains a 10-lb. load moved by a force acting parallel to the surface of the board?

42. A weight of 500 lbs. rests upon an inclined plane 20 ft. long and 8 ft. high. What must be the force of friction to keep it from sliding down the plane?

43. There is a uniform gate 4 ft. long and 3 ft. high which weighs 50 lbs. It is attached to a post by hinges at the top and bottom. (*a*) What horizontal pull or pressure must each of these hinges overcome? (*b*) What vertical pull? The load is divided equally between the hinges.

44. A uniformly thick board in the shape of an equilateral triangle 1 m. on a side and weighing 5 kg. is suspended with one of its sides vertical by means of hinges placed at the extremities of this side. What is the horizontal pull or pressure on each of these hinges?

45. A mass of 1 kg. is supported by a cord passing over a nail so that the two parts of the cord make an angle of 90° with each other. Find the tension on the cord.

46. A mass of 50 g. is attached to the center of a string passing over two frictionless pulleys so arranged that the angle between the two parts of the string on each side of the mass is 45°. How many grams must be attached to each end of the string after passing over the pulleys to keep the 50-g. mass in equilibrium?

47. A cord supporting a picture weighing 10 lbs. passes over a knob so that there is an angle of 60° between the two parts of the cord. How many pounds must the cord be able to support in order to hold the picture? [Plot.]

48. A rope 12 ft. long is attached to each end of a horizontal beam 8 ft. long. From the center of the rope is suspended a mass of 100 lbs. What is the tension on the rope?

49. A board 3 ft. square and weighing 10 lbs. is to be supported from a beam by two equal cords attached to the extremities of the upper edge of the board. (*a*) Will the cords need to be stronger if they are attached to the same point on the beam than if they extend vertically from their points of attachment on the board to points on the beam? (*b*) If so, how much stronger? The upper edge of the board is to be 3 ft. from the beam.

50. A picture weighing 25 lbs. is hung by a cord passing over a nail, the two parts of the cord making an angle of 120° with each other. What is the tension on the cord?

51. Two strings 6 and 10 ft. long, meeting at a point and making an angle of 60°, support a 50-lb. weight. What is the tension on each string?

52. A fish caught by a pole and line pulls with a force of 5 lbs. The inclination between the pole and the line is 45°. How many lbs. pull at right angles to its length must the pole be able to bear to keep it from breaking?

53. There is a rod 3 ft. long projecting horizontally from the side of a house, but not fastened to it. Four ft. vertically above the point where the rod joins the house there is a rope one end of which is attached to the house and the other to the outer end of the rod. From the point where the rope joins the rod is suspended a weight of 8 lbs. Find (a) the horizontal pressure exerted by the rod on the wall; (b) the tension on the rope. Consider the rod weightless.

54. A horizontal rod 10 cm. long is pivoted at one end and has attached to it 2 cm. from the pivot a weight of 50 g. How great a force acting on the free end at an angle of 45° to the rod will be required to keep the rod in a horizontal position?

55. A uniform beam 6 ft. long, weighing 50 lbs., has a rope 10 ft. long attached to its center. If the free end of the rope is attached to the wall 15 ft. above the ground, and the beam is placed in a horizontal position at right angles to the wall, with one end resting against the wall, what will be the tension on the rope?

56. In the previous problem what will be the pressure of the beam against the wall?

57. A beam 10 ft. long and weighing 100 lbs. leans against the side of a house, the top of the beam being 6 ft. above the ground. If its center of gravity is 6 ft. from the lower end of the beam, what will be the horizontal force exerted by the house? Disregard friction between beam and wall.

58. A ladder 20 ft. long and weighing 50 lbs. rests with one end against a smooth wall and the other end on the ground 8 ft. horizontally from the wall. The center of gravity of the ladder is 9 ft. from the base. (*a*) What is its horizontal pressure against the wall? (*b*) What is the horizontal force exerted by the ground?

59. A uniform beam 10 ft. long and weighing 50 lbs. leans against the side of a house, making an angle of 45° with it. Two ft. from the top of the beam is suspended a weight of 100 lbs. What is the horizontal pressure of the beam against the house? Disregard friction between house and beam.

60. A plumb bob weighing 5 lbs. is pushed aside by a horizontal force until the cord supporting it makes an angle of 60° with the vertical line. (*a*) How much does the cord now sustain? (*b*) How great is the horizontal force?

61. A uniform rod 1 m. long and weighing 1 kg. has one end resting upon the ground and is kept at an angle of 45° with the surface by a cord which is attached to the opposite end, and makes an angle of 90° with the rod. What is the tension on the cord?

62. The beam of a derrick makes an angle of 45° with the horizon, and the rope supporting the beam an angle of 45° with the beam. From the upper end of the beam is suspended a weight of 500 lbs. (*a*) What is the pressure on the beam? (*b*) What is the tension on the rope? Disregard the weight of the beam.

63. A square lot has a post at each corner. A rope is passed around these and tightened so that the tension upon it is 50 lbs. What is the pressure on each post?

64. A uniform rod, pivoted at one end, hangs vertically. If a force equal to ¼ the weight of the rod acts horizontally at the lower end, at what angle with the vertical will the rod be when in equilibrium?

FORCE AND ACCELERATION

$g = 32$ ft. per sec. per sec., or 980 cm. per sec. per sec.

Wherever the pound is used as a unit of force, unless otherwise stated, it is to be considered equal to 32 poundals; similarly, the gram force equals 980 dynes.

1. What will be the velocity of a freely falling body at the end of the 5th second? How far will it travel in the 6th second? The body starts from rest.

2. A body is acted upon by a force which imparts to it a velocity of 5 ft. per second. (*a*) How far will it go in 8 seconds from rest? (*b*) What will be the distance traveled in the last 3 seconds?

3. How far will a body move along a frictionless horizontal plane in 5 seconds from rest if it has a constant acceleration of 3 ft. per second per second?

4. In the previous problem how far will the body travel in the last half of the 5th second?

5. A body falling 4 seconds passes over 750 ft. What was its initial velocity?

6. How much velocity must be given to a body shot vertically upward in order that at the end of the 3d second it shall have a velocity of 100 ft. per second?

7. A body is shot upward with a velocity of 400 ft. per second. What velocity will it have after 15 seconds?

8. With how much vertical velocity must a bullet be shot into the air in order to fall back to its starting place in just 9 seconds after it left the gun?

9. In the previous problem, (a) how far will the bullet travel? (b) What will be the distances traveled in the 3d, 5th, and 9th seconds?

10. What initial velocity must a body have in order to rise 500 ft. against gravity?

11. A body has fallen 1000 ft. What is its velocity?

12. With what downward velocity must a body be thrown from a tower 500 ft. high in order to reach the ground in 5 seconds?

13. A body falls 5 seconds. How far does it fall (a) in the last half second? (b) in the first half second?

14. A body is thrown downward from a tower 500 ft. high with a velocity of 50 ft. per second. How long will it take to reach the ground?

15. Two masses of 50 and 100 g., respectively, are pulled toward each other by a mutual attraction of 10 dynes. What will be the velocity of each at the end of 5 seconds?

16. A body is passing along a frictionless horizontal plane with a constant acceleration of 20 ft. per second per second. How far does it go in the first half of the 5th second from rest?

17. What is the attraction of gravity in a place where a body falls 6 ft. in the first second?

18. A body shot vertically into the air returns to its starting point in 7½ seconds. (a) How far has it traveled? (b) What was its initial velocity? (c) How far did it travel in the 4th second?

19. A man is riding a bicycle at the rate of 15 miles an hour. How far will a package which he lets fall from a point 4 ft. above the ground move forward before striking the earth ?

20. From the top of a 50-ft. mast in a ship sailing at the rate of 10 miles an hour a cannon ball is dropped. How far back of the bottom of the mast will it strike the deck ?

21. A body thrown vertically downward from the top of a tower with a velocity of 20 ft. per second strikes the ground after 6 seconds. How high is the tower ?

22. With how much downward velocity must a body be thrown from a tower 500 ft. high in order to strike the ground in 5 seconds ?

23. How long will it take a force of 10 units acting on a mass of 40 to change its velocity from 15 to 20 ?

24. A body starting from rest and acted upon by a constant force acquires a velocity of 400 cm. per second in going 1000 cm. What was the acceleration ?

25. What must be the acceleration of a body to cause it to go 100 ft. in 5 seconds from rest ?

26. A body moves 15 ft. in one second and 21 in the next. (*a*) How long has it been moving with a uniform acceleration ? (*b*) How far will it go in the next 3 seconds ?

27. A body moves 20 ft. in one second and 28 in the next. (*a*) How long has it been moving ? (*b*) What is its acceleration ? (*c*) How far will it go in the next 10 seconds ?

28. A body weighing 5 lbs. and acted upon by a constant force moves 20 ft. along a frictionless horizontal plane in the 5th and 6th seconds from rest. What is the constant force ?

29. How long must a force of 10 poundals act on a mass of 30 lbs. to change its velocity from 5 to 25 ft. per second ?

30. In what distance will a force of 4 poundals be able to stop a mass of 10 lbs. moving at the rate of 20 ft. per second?

31. How far will a mass of 6 lbs. move in 6 seconds when acted upon by a constant force of 20 poundals?

32. What force will move 10 lbs. 40 ft. from rest in 4 seconds?

33. How long must a force of 8 poundals act on a mass of 6 lbs. to change its velocity from 4 to 12 ft. per second?

34. In what distance will a force of 4 poundals be able to stop a mass of 20 lbs. moving at the rate of 40 ft. per second?

35. A body weighing 5 lbs. and moving 60 ft. per second encounters a constant resistance of 20 poundals. How far will it move before stopping?

36. What is the least force that will move 20 lbs. 50 ft. from rest in 5 seconds?

37. A mass of 30 g. is moving with a velocity of 12 cm. per second. How great a force will bring it to rest in 5 seconds?

38. A body starts along a frictionless horizontal plane with a velocity of 30 ft. per second and travels 100 ft., receiving a constant acceleration. At the end of the 100 ft. it is moving at the rate of 50 ft. per second. (*a*) How long does it move? (*b*) What is the constant acceleration?

39. Find the time and acceleration of a body whose velocity changes (*a*) from 10 to 20 in going 100 ft.; (*b*) from 15 to 5.

40. Two bodies are dropped from the same place ½ of a second apart. After how long a time will the distance between them be 33 m.?

41. Two bodies are dropped successively from the same point, and after the second has been falling 5 seconds, are 20 m. apart. What was the interval of time between their release?

42. The deck of a ship is 20 ft. above the water. With how much horizontal velocity must a cannon ball be shot in order to strike a body floating, just submerged, 1000 ft. away? The mouth of the cannon is at the level of the deck.

43. A cannon ball is fired from the top of a vertical cliff 800 ft. high with a horizontal velocity of 1000 ft. per second. (*a*) How soon will it strike the level plain? (*b*) How far from a point directly beneath the cannon will the ball strike?

44. In the previous problem how far from the mouth of the cannon would the ball strike the plain ?

45. A stone is thrown from the top of a vertical cliff 40 ft. high with a horizontal velocity of 50 ft. per second. At what horizontal distance from the bottom of the cliff will it strike the ground?

46. A body shot from the top of a cliff with a horizontal velocity of 200 ft. per second strikes the ground at a horizontal distance of 1000 ft. from its starting point. How high is the cliff?

47. The length of a frictionless inclined plane is 1000 ft. and its height 600 ft. (*a*) How long will it take a body to slide down the plane? (*b*) What will be its velocity at the bottom ?

48. A body sliding down a frictionless inclined plane has at the end of the 3d second a velocity of 60 ft. per second. How far will it slide in 10 seconds ?

49. A body sliding down a frictionless inclined plane passes over 10 ft. the first second. How far will it travel in 5 seconds?

50. A block is sliding down a frictionless inclined plane and at the end of 5 seconds is traveling 4 m. per second. What time will be required for it to travel 20 m. from the starting point?

51. With what velocity must a body be shot up a frictionless inclined plane which rises 3 ft. in 5, in order to ascend to a vertical height of 36 ft.?

52. A vessel sailing at the rate of 20 ft. per second is just passing a lighthouse, when a ball falls from a mast 100 ft. high. How far in front of the lighthouse will it strike the deck?

53. A freely falling body passes the top of a tower 336 ft. high with a velocity of 64 ft. per second. It strikes the ground at the same instant that another body does, which started 3 seconds before it did. How far has the second body fallen?

54. A man standing on the edge of a cliff at the same instant shot a body vertically into the air and dropped another over the edge of the cliff. At the very instant the body shot into the air turns and begins to descend, the other strikes the ground. The distance between them at this instant is 1000 ft. What is the height of the cliff?

55. At the instant a body is dropped from the top of a tower 200 ft. high, another body is shot vertically into the air from the base of the tower, with a velocity of 200 ft. per second. How far above the bottom of the tower will they pass each other?

56. A ball is shot horizontally from the top of a vertical tower 480 ft. high with a velocity of 200 ft. per second; at the same instant a stone is thrown vertically downward with a velocity of 32 ft. per second. They both strike the ground at the same instant. (*a*) At what horizontal distance from the tower does the ball strike the ground? (*b*) What is the elevation of the ground above that at the foot of the tower?

57. A ball is thrown vertically upward with a velocity of 100 ft. per second from a balloon which is sinking at the rate of 20 ft. per second. How far will the balloon be from the ball at the instant the ball begins to fall?

58. An elevator is descending at a uniform rate of 16 ft. per second when a bundle is knocked off and falls to the floor of the building 100 ft. below. How long is it falling?

59. What is the distance in the previous problem between the bundle and the elevator at the instant the bundle strikes the floor?

60. An elevator moving downward with a uniform velocity of 20 ft. per second loosens a nail from the wall of the elevator well as it passes. The nail begins to fall when it is at a distance of 10 ft. above the floor of the elevator. How long before it will pass this floor in its fall?

61. A force of 10 g acting N. and another of 1000 dynes acting E. strike a ball weighing 100 g. What velocity will they give to the ball in 3 seconds?

62. A bucket weighing 20 lbs. is drawn up a well with a uniform acceleration of 5 ft. per second. What is the tension on the rope?

63. Attached to the ends of a rope passing over a frictionless pulley are two weights of 4 and 6 lbs., respectively. Supposing gravity alone acts on them, (*a*) how fast will they move? (*b*) in what direction?

64. A body of density 3 is dropped from the surface of the water. How long will it take it to sink to the bottom 500 ft. below? Neglect friction of water.

ENERGY

$g = 32$ ft. per sec. per sec., or 980 cm. per sec. per sec.

1. A stone weighing 50 g. is thrown with the velocity of 10 m. per second. What is its kinetic energy?

2. What is the kinetic energy of an engine weighing 100 tons moving at the rate of 40 miles per hour?

3. A body weighing 10 g. has fallen 5 seconds. What is its kinetic energy? What is its momentum?

4. A 4-oz. bullet is shot vertically upward with a velocity of 1000 ft. per second. (*a*) What is its kinetic energy when it leaves the gun? (*b*) How far will it rise?

5. A mass of 1 ton is raised 1 yd. What is its potential energy?

6. A body weighing 5 lbs. has fallen 200 ft. (*a*) What is its velocity? (*b*) What is its kinetic energy? (*c*) What is its momentum?

7. With what velocity must a 10-g. mass move in order to strike a target with a kinetic energy of 500 ergs?

8. A stone weighing 20 g. is thrown vertically upward with a velocity of 39.2 m. per second. What is its kinetic energy at the end of the second second?

9. What is the momentum and what is the kinetic energy of a 25-g. ball, free to fall, which has fallen 5 seconds?

10. Compare the momenta, velocities, and energies, respectively, of a cannon of mass "M" and its ball of mass "m," after discharge, if both are free to move.

11. How high must a mass of 10 lbs. be raised in order that it may have a potential energy of 500 ft. lbs.? With what velocity will it strike the ground if allowed to fall?

12. A pile driver weighs 100 lbs. and falls until it acquires a velocity of 50 ft. per second. With what energy will it strike?

13. In the previous problem with how much energy would the pile driver strike if it fell from the height of 50 ft.?

14. A bullet weighing 20 g. is shot vertically into the air and returns to its starting place in 10 seconds. With what kinetic energy did it leave the gun? Disregard resistance of the air.

15. Compare the kinetic energy of a 1-lb. mass moving at the rate of 500 ft. per second and that of a 500-lb. mass moving at the rate of 1 ft. per second.

16. A stone weighing 4 oz. falls until it acquires a velocity of 256 ft. per second. (*a*) How much kinetic energy has it? (*b*) How far has it fallen?

17. What is the mass of a body that has a kinetic energy of 500 ft. lbs. after falling freely for 4 seconds?

18. What must be the mass of a body that, after falling freely for 3 seconds, will strike with an energy of 360 ft. lbs.?

19. A body weighing 20 g. has a kinetic energy of 1000 ergs. How far would it ascend vertically?

20. A ball weighing 1 lb. has a velocity of 100 ft. per second. (*a*) How far will it rise vertically? (*b*) How far will it ascend if the velocity is doubled? (*c*) How far will it ascend if the weight is doubled, the velocity remaining the same?

21. A mass weighing 150 lbs. starts from rest and attains a speed of 30 ft. per second. How many ft. lbs. of energy have been exerted upon it to give it this velocity?

22. What is the kinetic energy, expressed in ergs, of a mass of 100 g. moving at the rate of 80 cm. per second?

23. In the previous problem how many dynes of force must act upon this mass to bring it to rest in 10 seconds?

24. A body weighing 1 lb. is shot vertically into the air with a velocity of 32 ft. per second. How much kinetic energy has it at the end of $\frac{1}{4}$ of a second?

25. A cannon ball weighing 10 lbs. is discharged with a velocity of 320 ft. per second. What is its kinetic energy in ft. lbs.?

26. A body weighing $\frac{1}{2}$ a lb. is thrown vertically downward with a velocity of 20 ft. per second and strikes the ground in 3 seconds. With how much energy does it strike?

27. With how much energy must a body weighing 4 oz. be thrown vertically upward in order to return to its starting place in 5 seconds?

28. A body weighing 8 g. is shot vertically upward and rises 8 seconds. What is its kinetic energy at the end of 5 seconds?

29. A body weighing 10 lbs. is shot vertically into the air and 10 seconds elapse before it returns to its starting place. (*a*) How far did it travel in the entire time? (*b*) How far in the 6th second? (*c*) With what energy, the resistance of the air not being considered, did it strike the ground?

30. A stone weighing 2 lbs. is thrown vertically downward from the top of a tower 300 ft. high and strikes the ground with an energy of 650 ft. lbs. With what velocity was it thrown?

31. A 1-lb. mass is thrown vertically upward and at the end of 1 second is moving at the rate of 96 ft. per second. How much energy will it have on reaching the ground?

32. A force of 10 lbs. acts for 3 seconds on a mass of 3 lbs. (*a*) How much kinetic energy will the mass have? (*b*) how much velocity?

33. With how much energy must a bullet weighing 20 g. be shot horizontally from a gun 4 m. above a level plane in order to strike the ground 150 m. away from the gun?

34. If a body weighing 1 lb. ascends to a certain vertical height, how far will another body weighing 2 lbs. ascend if it has the same initial energy?

35. A mass of 5 g. is acted upon by a constant force of 100 dynes for 6 seconds. What will be its energy at the end of 6 seconds?

36. If a cannon throwing a 10-lb. ball is trained to shoot vertically upward and is then discharged with enough powder to give an initial velocity of 500 ft. per second to the ball, find the kinetic energy of the ball when $\frac{1}{3}$ the distance to its maximum height.

37. In the previous problem how many horse-power of energy have been expended when the cannon ball has risen $\frac{1}{3}$ its maximum height?

38. Energy is supplied to a pump at the bottom of a mine shaft 800 ft. below the surface, at the rate of 30 horse-power. How many cu. ft. of water will be raised per hour if all the energy is utilized in raising water?

39. A ball of weight 8 oz., and thrown vertically downward with a velocity of 25 ft. per second, has how much kinetic energy when it leaves the hands of the thrower? What will be its kinetic energy at a point 150 ft. from the thrower?

40. If 100 cu. ft. of water pass over a dam 10 ft. high in 1 minute, how much energy could be derived from this if all were utilized? A cu. ft. of water weighs 62.5 lbs.

41. If the diameter of the earth were doubled, its density remaining the same, with how much energy would a mass of 1 lb. falling from a height of 30 ft. above the surface strike the ground?

42. A body weighing 10 lbs. is moving along a horizontal plane with an initial velocity of 64 ft. per second; the coefficient of friction is $\frac{1}{4}$. What will its energy be 2 seconds before it stops?

43. A 5-lb. mass resting upon a frictionless horizontal plane is acted upon by a constant force which gives it an acceleration of 10 ft. per second per second. What will be its energy at the end of 8 seconds?

44. A body weighing 1 lb. started from rest and acted upon by a constant force moves 10 ft. in the 5th second. What is its energy at the end of this second?

45. A body weighing 5 lbs. and acted upon by a constant force moves 20 ft. along a frictionless horizontal plane in the 5th and 6th seconds from rest. (*a*) What is its acceleration? (*b*) What will be its energy at the end of the 8th second from rest?

46. A body weighing 5 lbs. moves along a frictionless horizontal plane 30 ft. in the 3d and 4th seconds from rest. What is the acceleration, and what will be the energy of the body at the end of the 10th second?

47. A mass of 10 g. is shot along a horizontal plane with a velocity of 80 cm. per second and encounters a constant resistance of 20 dynes. What will be its energy at the end of the 4th second?

48. A body weighing 1 lb. moving along a horizontal plane with a velocity of 100 ft. per second encounters a constant resistance equal to $\frac{1}{4}$ its weight. What will be its energy in ft. lbs. after the resistance has acted for 3 seconds?

49. A pendulum bob weighing 1 lb. swings to a height of 4 in. above its lowest point. With what kinetic energy does it pass this point, and what becomes of this energy as it moves on?

50. What initial velocity is necessary, in case of a projected ball, to strike a target 200 ft. above the starting place with a velocity of 100 ft. per second? Disregard the resistance of the air.

51. A balloon is ascending vertically at the rate of 16 ft. per second when a body weighing 1 lb. is dropped overboard. What will be the kinetic energy of the body at the end of the 1st second?

52. A man standing on a platform 10 ft. above the ground with a 25-lb. weight in his hand jumps off. (*a*) How much pressure does the weight exert upon his hand while he is falling? (*b*) How much kinetic energy has it the moment he strikes the ground?

53. Two boys are passing a ball which weighs 4 oz. from end to end of a closed car 60 ft. long which is moving at the rate of 50 ft. per second. With how much greater energy must one of the boys impel the ball than the other?

54. The eaves of a house are 32 ft. from the ground. A body weighing 1 lb. starts from the ridgepole of the house, slides off and drops to the ground. The roof is 48 ft. long and rises 2 ft. in every 3 ft. of length of incline. With how much energy does the body strike the ground? The coefficient of friction is $\frac{1}{10}$.

55. A body weighing 1 lb., started with an initial velocity of 16 ft. per second down a frictionless inclined plane 80 ft. long and rising 1 ft. in 5, strikes a horizontal plane having a coefficient of friction of $\frac{1}{4}$. What will be its energy after it has passed over 20 ft. of this plane?

56. A body weighing 2 lbs. slides 100 ft. down an inclined plane rising 3 ft. in 5. What is its energy at the bottom of the incline? Coefficient of friction is $\frac{1}{10}$.

57. A body weighing 50 lbs. is projected 10 ft. up a frictionless inclined plane rising 3 ft. in 5. (*a*) With what energy did the body start? (*b*) With what velocity did it start?

58. With how much energy must a body weighing 1 lb. be shot up an inclined plane rising 3 ft. in 5, to move 20 ft. along this plane? Coefficient of friction is $\frac{1}{4}$.

59. Two balls of 10 and 100 g. mass, situated 1100 cm. distant from each other, are attracted toward each other by a constant force of 100 dynes. What will be the energy and momentum of each of these balls when they come together?

60. A body weighing 1 lb. is projected with a velocity of 100 ft. per second in the direction of a car's motion, from a car moving at the rate of 1 mile a minute. What will be its energy at the moment of projection?

61. With what energy must a body weighing 1 g. be shot vertically upward to be able to do 1000 ergs of work after rising 3 seconds?

62. A body weighing 1 lb. falls 196 ft. and strikes the ground. It rebounds with $\frac{3}{4}$ its former energy. How many seconds will pass before it strikes the ground again?

63. With what energy must a ball weighing 10 lbs. be shot vertically upward in order to rise 200 ft. and strike a target with a velocity of 300 ft. per second? Disregard resistance of the air.

64. A body weighing 8 g. is shot vertically upward with a velocity of 490 m. per second. What is its total energy at the end of the 5th second? What is its kinetic energy at the end of the 3d second?

WORK

1. How much work must be done in moving a mass of 10 lbs. on a horizontal surface 100 ft.? Coefficient of friction is ⅓.

2. How much work is done in pulling a body weighing 40 lbs. 20 ft. along a frictionless inclined plane that rises 1 ft. in 5 of horizontal distance?

3. How many ergs of work will be required to raise 2 kg. 1 m. when intensity of gravity is 980?

4. A mass of 50 g. is at a place 100 cm. above a level plain. What is its energy of position in regard to the plain? Intensity of gravity is 980.

5. How much work is done in raising 100 cu. ft. of water 50 ft.? Suppose the operation took 1 hour, express the answer in horse-power.

6. How much work is done against gravity in rolling a 200-lb. barrel of flour into a wagon whose floor is 3 ft. 6 in. above the initial position of the barrel?

7. A man draws a pail of water weighing 75 lbs. from the cellar to the first floor, a distance of 15 ft. How much work does he do?

8. A wheel weighing 100 lbs. encounters an obstacle — a cube 6 in. on a side. How much work is done against gravity in surmounting the obstacle?

9. By using a lever a man raises a stone of unknown weight $\frac{1}{10}$ of a foot. His lever is 22 ft. long, of the first class, and the fulcrum is 2 ft. from the stone. He exerts a force of 100 lbs. If the lever is weightless, how much work does he do?

10. In the previous problem how much work would the man do in raising the stone if the lever were uniform and weighed 60 lbs.? How much pressure would he exert?

11. In a place where gravity is 32, how much work must be done upon a body weighing 5 lbs. to give it a vertical velocity of 100 ft. per second?

12. A well was dug 10 ft. deep and 4 ft. in diameter. How much work was done in raising the dirt to the level of the surface if a cu. ft. of dirt weighs 150 lbs.?

13. A hammer with a uniform handle 3 ft. long and weighing 2 lbs. has at the end of the handle a cylindrical head 4 in. in diameter and weighing 10 lbs. The hammer is suspended from the end of the handle in a vertical position. How much work will be required to raise the hammer to a horizontal position?

14. A uniform pole 10 ft. long weighing 8 lbs., pivoted at the upper end and hanging vertically, has attached to the lower end a weight of 20 lbs. How much work must be done in order to bring pole and weight to a horizontal position?

15. If the clouds were 1 mile above the earth, and rain enough fell to cover 1 square mile at sea level ½ in. deep, how much work was done in raising the water to the clouds? From what did the energy come?

16. There is an anchor weighing 2000 lbs. to be raised by a capstan the axis of which is 2 ft. in diameter. Four handspikes, each 6 ft. long, are to be used. A man pushes at the end of each handspike, and another 2 ft. from the end. If each man exerts the same amount of force, how much must he exert? Disregard friction. Each handspike extends into the center of the capstan.

17. The length of a frictionless inclined plane is 20 ft. and its height is 8 ft. (*a*) How much work is done against gravity in pushing a body weighing 10 lbs. up the plane? (*b*) What would be its velocity if allowed to slide down the plane? $g = 32$.

18. A boy who can push 50 lbs. wishes to roll a barrel weighing 200 lbs. into a wagon 2½ ft. high. How long a board must he procure and how much work will he do in getting the barrel into the wagon?

19. A weight of 10 lbs. rests upon an inclined plane rising 3 ft. in 5 of incline. If the friction is just enough to keep the body from sliding down the plane, how much work must be done in raising the body to a height of 12 ft. by means of the inclined plane?

20. A body weighing 10 lbs. is pulled 20 ft. along an inclined plane which rises 3 ft. in 5 of incline, coefficient of friction being ½. How much work is done?

21. A 100-lb. bale of hay 2 × 2 × 4 ft. lies on a barn floor. It is to be raised 20 ft. to the loft by means of a rope weighing ½ lb. to the foot. How much work must be done to raise the hay?

22. Two connected vessels whose cross-sections are 10 and 5 sq. ft., respectively, have their bases on a common level, but the water in the larger vessel stands at 20 ft. depth, while that in the smaller is only 5 ft. deep. How much work does gravity do in bringing the water to a common level?

23. An elevator with its load weighs 1500 lbs. It is supported by 4 wire cables, each weighing 6 lbs. to the ft., and each 100 ft. long. How much work is done, friction aside, in raising the elevator 30 ft. from its lowest position? [*The elevator is raised by winding the cable about a drum.*]

24. How much work must be done on a bullet weighing 25 g. to give it a muzzle velocity of 35,000 cm. per second ?

25. A boulder weighing 10 tons totters on the edge of a perpendicular cliff 900 ft. high.   What is its energy of position with respect to the level 900 ft. below?   How much work has been done against gravity in lifting the boulder to its present position ?

26. A mass of 25 g. starts from rest and after a short time is found to be moving with a velocity of 5 m. per second.   How much work has been done upon it ?

27. There is a ladder 10 ft. long resting against a wall and making an angle of 45° with the surface of the ground. How much work will be done by a man carrying 100 lbs. of bricks up the ladder and placing them upon the wall 5 ft. above the end of the ladder ?

COEFFICIENT OF FRICTION

1. A body is projected along a horizontal plane with a velocity of 100 ft. per second, coefficient of friction being $\frac{1}{10}$.   How far will it go before coming to rest ?

2. A body is thrown on the ice with a velocity of 30 ft. per second.   If the coefficient of friction between the body and the ice be $\frac{1}{10}$, (*a*) how soon will it stop? (*b*) how far will it travel ?

3. With what velocity must a body be moving in order, before coming to rest, to pass over 20 ft. on a horizontal plane, the coefficient of friction of which is $\frac{1}{4}$?

4. A body moves 10 ft. along a horizontal plane before coming to rest.   The coefficient of friction is $\frac{1}{10}$.   With what velocity must the body have started ?

5. What is the coefficient of friction of a horizontal plane if a body shot with a velocity of 48 ft. per second moves 108 ft. before coming to rest?

6. A body moves with a velocity of 60 ft. per second along a horizontal plane, and is brought to rest after passing over 200 ft. of the plane. What is the coefficient of friction?

7. A body moving along a horizontal plane with a velocity of 100 ft. per second encounters a constant resistance equal to $\frac{1}{5}$ of its weight. How far will it go before coming to rest?

8. What must be the coefficient of friction of a horizontal plane so that a body moving with a velocity of 30 ft. per second will come to rest after moving 100 ft.?

9. What is the coefficient of friction when a body moving along a horizontal plane with a velocity of 50 ft. per second comes to rest after moving 50 ft.?

10. A 4-lb. mass moving at the rate of 500 ft. per second is acted upon by a force which tends to stop it. The mass comes to rest after it has gone 25 ft. How large is this force?

11. A mass of 20 g. moving with a velocity of 50 cm. per second encounters a constant resistance of 10 dynes. How far will it move before coming to rest? How long will it move?

12. A body moving with a velocity of 50 ft. per second encounters a constant resistance which brings it to rest after it has passed over 25 ft. What is the ratio of resistance to the weight of the body?

13. A body moves along a frictionless horizontal plane with a velocity of 60 ft. per second. After traveling 200 ft. it comes to rest. What is the ratio between its weight and the average resistance of the air?

14. A block, after sliding 25 ft. along a frictionless inclined plane which rises 3 ft. in 5, strikes a horizontal plane which has a coefficient of friction of $\frac{1}{4}$. How far will it move before coming to rest?

15. A body weighing 10 lbs. is pushed 20 ft. along an inclined plane rising 3 ft. in 5. If the coefficient of friction between the block and plane is $\frac{1}{4}$, how much work has been done?

16. A body weighing 100 lbs. is pushed up an inclined plane 30 ft. high. The coefficient of friction is $\frac{1}{4}$. How much work is done? The incline rises 6 ft. in 10.

17. A body slides down an inclined plane rising 3 ft. in 5. If the coefficient of friction is $\frac{1}{5}$, find the velocity gained in passing over 20 ft. of the plane.

18. How far will the body of the previous problem move if it passes onto a horizontal plane? Coefficient of friction is $\frac{1}{5}$.

19. A body moves 20 ft. along a horizontal plane whose coefficient of friction is $\frac{4}{10}$, and then rises 10 ft. along a frictionless inclined plane rising 3 ft. in 5. Find the initial velocity.

20. If in the previous problem the body slides back down the inclined plane, how far will it move along the horizontal plane?

21. What must be the coefficient of friction on an inclined plane rising 1 ft. in 4, so that it shall take 100 ft. lbs. of work to raise an 8-lb. mass 10 ft. vertically?

22. With what velocity must a body weighing 10 lbs. be started in order to move 50 ft. along a horizontal plane having a coefficient of friction of $\frac{1}{5}$? With what energy must it start?

23. A body sliding 20 ft. along a rough inclined plane descends vertically 16 ft. If the coefficient of friction between the block and the plane is $\frac{1}{5}$, what velocity will the body acquire?

24. A boy capable of exerting a force of 20 lbs. wishes to raise a mass of 50 lbs. to a height of 4 ft. What is the shortest frictionless plank that he can use as an inclined plane to do this? If coefficient of friction equals $\frac{1}{3}$, how much aid will he require to do it?

25. In the previous problem how much work will he do? How much work will his helper do?

26. If a mass of 1 mgm. resting on a horizontal plane is acted on by a force of 1 dyne for 10 seconds, what velocity will the mass acquire in the time if coefficient of friction is 1?

27. What will be the kinetic energy of the mass of the previous problem and how far will it move in the 10 seconds?

28. A mass of 1000 lbs. rests on an incline. How much work must be done in drawing the body 20 ft. up the incline, if the projection of the incline on the horizontal is 16 ft. and the coefficient of friction $\frac{1}{4}$?

29. A pair of horses capable of pulling with a force of 4000 lbs. are attached to a loaded dray which weighs 10 tons. If the coefficient of friction is $\frac{1}{10}$, how steep an incline can they ascend?

30. A body sliding down a rough inclined plane travels 10 ft. along the plane, but descends only 6 ft. vertically. If the force of friction is equal to $\frac{1}{4}$ the weight of the body, find the velocity gained during the descent.

31. A block weighing 50 lbs. rests on an incline such that the block must move 5 ft. to rise 3 ft. The coefficient of friction is .25 How much work must be done by a force parallel to the incline in drawing the block 30 ft.?

32. A 5-lb. weight hanging over the edge of a table drags a 10-lb. weight along the table. The coefficient of friction is $\frac{1}{10}$. How fast does the weight move?

33. A 5-lb. weight hanging over the edge of a table drags a 25-lb. weight along it. If the coefficient of friction between the table and the 25-lb. weight is $\frac{1}{10}$, find the acceleration.

34. A mass of 10 lbs. rests upon a table; the coefficient of friction is $\frac{2}{3}$. It is acted upon by a 5-lb. weight hanging over the edge of the table. Find the distance passed over by the weight in 1 second.

35. A boat weighing 2 tons is moving at the rate of 10 miles per hour when the engine breaks. If the coefficient of resistance of the water is $\frac{2}{3}$, how far will the boat go before it stops?

GRAVITATION

1. How far above the surface of the earth must a 50-g. ball be taken in order that it may weigh 10 g.?

2. How far above the surface of the earth will 1 lb. avoirdupois weigh 4 oz.? How far below?

3. How much would a mass that weighs 100 lbs. 1000 miles below the surface of the earth weigh 3000 miles above the surface?

4. How much would a mass that weighs 1 lb. 2000 miles above the surface of the earth weigh 2000 miles below the surface?

5. If a body weighs 20 lbs. on the surface of the earth, what will be its weight 1000 miles below the surface?

6. What ratio will the mass of a 1-lb. weight, at a point 1000 miles from the center of the earth, bear to the mass needed to weigh 1 lb. at the surface of the earth?

7. If the diameter of the moon is $\frac{1}{4}$, and its mass $\frac{1}{80}$ that of the earth, what would be the weight of a mass of 1 lb. upon the surface of the moon?

8. Suppose the mass of the earth were increased ¼. How much would one of our present pound weights then weigh?

9. A mass of 10 g. is 100 cm. distant from another mass of 1 g. What ratio does the attraction of the 10-g. mass for the 1-g. mass bear to that of the 1-g. for the 10-g.?

10. How would it affect the attraction between the earth and moon to double the mass of both?

11. Suppose the distance of the moon were doubled, what effect would it have upon its attraction for the earth?

12. If the mass of the earth were doubled and that of the moon were trebled, how would this affect their attraction for each other?

13. If the volume of the sun should decrease ½, its mass remaining the same, what effect would this have upon its attraction for masses upon its surface?

14. Suppose the sun were 4 times as far away, how would this affect its attraction for the earth?

15. The mass of 1 lb. is carried to such a distance above the earth that it weighs but 15 oz. What is the acceleration due to gravity at this point? The acceleration on the surface is 32 ft. per second per second.

16. How far above the surface of the earth will 1 lb. avoirdupois weigh only 1 oz.? What is the acceleration due to gravity at this point?

17. If the diameter of the earth is 8000 miles, with what acceleration will a body 1200 miles above the surface of the earth tend to fall?

18. Jupiter has 316 times as much matter in it as the earth, and its diameter is 11 times that of the earth. A body on the earth falls with an acceleration of 32 ft. per second per second. What will be its acceleration per second on Jupiter?

19. Two balls, one weighing 5 lbs. and the other 8 lbs., are distant from a third 10 and 15 ft., respectively. What is their relative attraction for the third ball?

20. Two bodies which mutually attract each other have their masses increased 2 and 3 fold, respectively. How much must the distance between them be increased to keep their attraction for each other the same as it was before the masses were increased?

21. If the distance between two bodies is increased 3 fold, how much must the product of their masses be increased to keep their mutual attraction the same?

22. The relative masses of two bodies are as 2:3, and their relative distances from a third are as 4·5. What is their relative attraction for the third?

23. The attractions of two bodies for a third are as 3:4, and their masses as 2:3. What are their relative distances?

24. The attractions of two bodies for a third are as 3.8, and their distances as 4:3. What are their relative masses?

25. The mass of the earth is about 80 times that of the moon, and their distance apart is 240,000 miles. At what distance from the earth in the line joining their centers of gravity would a mass be equally attracted by each of these bodies?

26. If the mass of the earth is 80 times the mass of the moon, and the distance between them is 240,000 miles, what ratio will the attraction of the earth, for a body situated 120,000 miles from its center on a line joining the centers of gravity of the earth and moon, bear to the attraction of the moon for that body?

27. If *g* equals 32 ft. per second per second at the surface of the earth, what will it be at a point 40,000 miles from the surface of the earth?

28. If the earth and moon were to be drawn together by their mutual attraction, at what distance from the point at present occupied by the earth would the impact take place?

29. The diameters of the earth and moon are 7900 and 2160 miles, respectively. Their sp. grs. are 5.6 and 3.5. If a body upon the earth weighs 100 lbs., what would it weigh upon the moon?

30. The equatorial diameter of the earth is about 7925, and the polar diameter about 7900 miles. How much will a mass which, by the indication of a spring balance, weighs 1 ton at the equator, weigh at the pole?

PENDULUMS

The length of a seconds pendulum in the latitude of New York is 39.1 in. $g = 32.16$.

1. What is the length of a pendulum that will beat 4 times in 3 seconds?

2. What is the length of a pendulum that beats (a) $\frac{1}{2}$ a second? (b) $\frac{1}{4}$ a second?

3. What is the length of a pendulum that vibrates 5 times in 4 seconds?

4. A clock whose pendulum beats seconds gains 2 minutes a day. How much too short is the pendulum?

5. If one pendulum vibrates once a second and another pendulum vibrates 3 times in 2 seconds, what are the relative lengths of the two pendulums?

6. How long must a pendulum be to make 3 vibrations while a pendulum 70 cm. long is making 2 vibrations?

7. If the times of vibration of 2 pendulums are as 2 : 3, what are their relative lengths?

8. A certain pendulum makes 3 vibrations while another makes 4. What are their relative lengths?

9. If a pendulum makes 5 vibrations while another is making 2, what are the relative lengths of the two pendulums?

10. What must be the relative lengths of two pendulums if one vibrates 3 times as fast as the other?

11. If a pendulum 2 m. long vibrates 42 times in a minute, what is the length of a pendulum that vibrates 84 times in a minute?

12. A clock whose pendulum beats $\frac{1}{2}$ a second is found to gain 30 seconds a day in the winter. How much has the pendulum contracted?

13. The length of a pendulum being increased $\frac{1}{3}$, what is the ratio of decrease of vibrations in a given time?

14. If on account of a change in the length of a pendulum the number of vibrations in a given time has been increased $\frac{1}{4}$, what part of its length has the pendulum been shortened?

15. When two pendulums are hung side by side, one of them is found to make 5 more vibrations in 3 minutes than the other. If the first pendulum is 60 cm. long, how long is the other? The length of a seconds pendulum is 993.3 mm.

16. Find the length of a seconds pendulum at the poles; g is 32.25.

17. In what time would a seconds pendulum vibrate when placed at a distance of 8000 miles above the surface of the earth?

18. If a seconds pendulum is placed at a distance of 2000 miles below the surface of the earth, what will be its time of vibration?

19. What will be the value of g in a place where a pendulum 39.2 in. long beats seconds?

20. How high must a balloon rise above the surface of the earth to cause a seconds pendulum which it carries to beat 58 times a minute?

21. A seconds pendulum on being carried to the top of a mountain is found to vibrate but 57 times in a minute. What is the acceleration of gravity at this point?

22. At the bottom of a mine in the latitude of New York a pendulum which at the surface beats seconds is found to make but 59 vibrations in a minute. What is the depth of the mine?

23. If the acceleration due to gravity at the surface of the sun is 28 times as great as at the surface of the earth, what would be the length of a seconds pendulum there?

24. If the squares of the times of vibration at two points are inversely as the forces of gravity at those points, what is the relation between the times of vibration and the distances of the points of vibration from the center of the earth?

25. The diameter of the earth is 7900 and of the moon 2160 miles. The average density of the earth is 5.6 and of the moon 3.5. How long a time of vibration would a pendulum have on the moon if it vibrates once a second on the surface of the earth?

LEVERS, INCLINED PLANE, CENTER OF GRAVITY

1. What weight can be lifted by a lever of the first class, with a power of 200 lbs., the weight-arm being 6 in. and the power-arm 2.5 ft.?

2. The arms of a lever of the first class are 8 in. and 24 in. What load on the longer arm will balance 150 lbs. on the shorter arm?

3. A man uses an 8-ft. crowbar for lifting a stone of 800 lbs. weight. He thrusts the bar under the stone until the distance from the end of the bar that rests on the earth to the point of contact of bar and stone is 1 ft. With what force must the man lift on the other end of the bar?

4. If the man had raised the stone of Problem 3 by putting one end of the bar under the stone and a fulcrum 1 ft. from that point, what would have been the value, in lbs. weight, of his push down at the other end of the lever?

5. Two men, C and D, carry a load of 500 lbs. on a pole between them. The men are 10 ft. apart, and the load is 4 ft. from C. Find the amount of each man's lift.

6. The head of a claw-hammer is of such length that the distance from a nail between the claws to the point of contact between the hammer and timber holding the nail is 4 in. The handle of the hammer is 1.5 ft. long. If a force of 25 lbs. is applied at the end of the handle normal to it, what is the force at the nail?

7. A and B sustain upon their shoulders a weight of 300 lbs., placed on a bar 18 ft. long. The weight is placed 12 ft. from A. What is the weight borne by each man?

8. A weightless rod 10 ft. long is balanced at a point 3 ft. from one end. What weight hung from this end will be supported by 12 lbs. hung from the other?

9. A uniform lever 10 ft. long balances about a point 1 ft. from one end when loaded at that end with 50 lbs. Find the weight of the lever.

10. A uniform bar 20 ft. long and weighing 100 lbs. rests in a horizontal position on a support 6 ft. from one end. A load of 100 lbs. is suspended from the end of the long arm of the bar. What load applied at the end of the short arm will produce equilibrium?

11. A weightless bar 1 m. in length is graduated in deci-meters, and at the end of the 1st and 8th graduations are attached 1 and 9 g., respectively. Where is the center of gravity of the combination?

12. A bar 16 ft. long and weighing 20 lbs. is in a hori-zontal position, and bears at one end a load of 80 lbs. The center of gravity of the bar is 6 ft. from the end carry-ing the 80 lbs. load. A load of 40 lbs. is placed on the other end of the bar. 'Where must a fulcrum be placed that the whole may be in equilibrium?

13. A bar 12 ft. long and weighing 12 lbs. has a load of 12 lbs. on one end and a load of 20 lbs. on the other. The whole is in equilibrium when supported at its middle point. Where is the center of gravity of the bar?

14. Two equal weights of 10 lbs. each are hung one at each end of a bar which weighs 5 lbs. and is 6 ft. long. The bar thus weighted balances about a point 3 in. distant from the center of its length. Find its center of gravity.

15. A straight lever 10 ft. long, when unweighted, bal-ances about a point 4 ft. from one end; but when loaded with 20 lbs. at this end and 4 lbs. at the other, it balances at a point 3 ft. from the end. Find the weight of the lever.

16. On one arm of a false balance a body weighs 11 lbs.; on the other, 17 lbs. 4 oz. What is the true weight?

17. In one pan of a false balance a piece of meat weighs 1 lb. 8 oz.; in the other, 2 lbs. 4 oz. What is the true weight?

18. Two weights keep a horizontal, weightless bar at rest. The pressure on the fulcrum is 10 lbs., the difference of the weights 4 lbs., and the difference of the lever arms 9 in. What are the weights and their lever arms?

19. A uniform straight lever 10 ft. long balances at a point 3 ft. from one end, when 12 lbs. are hung from this

end, and an unknown weight from the other.   The lever
itself weighs 8 lbs.   Find the unknown weight.

20. A uniform beam 12 ft. long rests upon two posts
3 and 5 ft., respectively, from each end.   How much must
be sawed off from the 5-ft. end to make the weight supported by its post twice that supported by the other?

21. A bent lever, *ACB*, has the arm *AC*, 3 ft.; *CB*,
8 ft.; *P*, 5 lbs.; and the angle *ACB*, 140°.   What weight
must be attached at *B* in order to keep *AC* horizontal?
P acts from *A* vertically downward.   [Olmstead.]

22. A circular hole 2 in. in diameter is cut in a uniform
circular disc 6 in. in diameter.   The centers being 1 in.
apart, find the center of gravity of the disc.

23. Find the center of gravity of weights of 7, 6, 9, and
2 lbs. arranged at the corners of a square 1 ft. on a side.

24. Weights of 1, 3, 5, and 7 lbs. are placed at the corners of a uniform square plate which is 10 in. on a side
and weighs 4 lbs.   Find the center of gravity of the system.

25. A square 1 ft. on a side has weights of 1, 2, 3, and
4 lbs. placed at each of its corners.   Where is the center of
gravity of the weights?

26. A square 1 ft. on a side has weights of 2, 4, 6, and
8 g. placed at the corners.   Find the center of gravity of
the square.

27. A circular board 2 ft in diameter and of uniform
thickness has a circular hole 6 in. in diameter cut in it
tangent to its circumference   How far from the center of
the board is its center of gravity?

28. One of the 4 triangles into which a square is divided
by its diagonals is removed.   Find the distance of the center of gravity of the remainder from the intersection of the
diagonals.

29. A square is divided into 4 equal squares, and one of these is removed. Find the distance of the center of gravity of the remaining portion from the center of the original square.

30. A body weighing 1000 lbs. rests on an incline 5 ft. long and 3 ft. high. What force is required to draw the body up the incline (*a*) if acting parallel to the incline? (*b*) acting parallel to the base? Neglect friction.

31. The height, base, and length of an inclined plane are 6, 8, and 10 ft. What weight will be held on the incline by a force of 100 lbs. (*a*) parallel to the base? (*b*) parallel to the incline? Neglect friction.

32. A mass of 50 lbs. rests on an incline such that it must move 10 ft. in order to rise 6 ft. What force parallel to the incline will be needed to draw the mass 5 ft.?

33. The bottom of a wagon body is 4 ft. above the ground. A plank 12 ft. long is placed with one end on the ground, the other on the wagon body. What force must a man exert in order to roll a 300-lb. barrel of sugar up this plank?

34. If the force of Problem 33 is exerted parallel to the earth, how large will it need to be?

35. A sled is at rest on a hill that rises 1 ft. in 3. The weight of the sled is 100 lbs. What force parallel to the slope will be required to hold the sled in place? Neglect friction.

MACHINES

Disregard friction and slipping of belts. $\pi = 3\frac{1}{7}$.

1. The pulley on the headstock of a lathe is 3 in. in diameter. This is belted to an 8-in. pulley on a shaft that makes 420 revolutions per minute. At what rate will a block of wood placed in the chuck revolve?

2. The pulley on the armature shaft of a dynamo is 4 in. in diameter. This is to be belted to a driving shaft which makes 500 revolutions per minute. The speed of the dynamo must be 1700 revolutions per minute. What must be the size of the pulley placed on the shaft?

3. If the wheel of a bicycle is 28 in. in diameter, the small sprocket 3 in., and the driving sprocket 8 in., how many times will a man need to move his right foot up and down in going a mile?

4. A shaft has upon it two pulleys, each 8 in. in diameter. The speed of the shaft is 400 revolutions per minute. What must be the size of the pulleys of two machines if when belted to the shaft one of them has a speed of 300 revolutions per minute and the other of 900?

5. A shaft which makes 300 revolutions per minute has a 6-in. pulley upon it. This pulley is belted to the pulley on a drum 3 ft. in diameter. If the drum is to wind off 1000 yds. of yarn per minute, what must be the size of its pulley?

6. If the wheels of an electric car are 2 ft., the axle cog-wheel 8 in., and the cog-wheel attached to the motor 12 in. in diameter, what must be the speed of the motor to carry the car a mile in 5 minutes?

7. Four cog-wheels, 10, 8, 6, and 4 in. in diameter, are placed in the same vertical plane with their cogs fitting to each other. There is a weight of 10 lbs. hung from the outside end of the horizontal diameter of the 10-in. wheel. How many pounds must be hung from the outside end of the horizontal diameter of the 4-in. wheel to balance this?

8. Four men are working at a capstan. They walk in a circle of 7 ft. diameter and each exerts a force of 50 lbs.

Each time they traverse the circle there are 2 ft. of rope pulled in. What is the resistance overcome?

9. The rope from a hand elevator is wound around an axle 4 in. in diameter. The wheel attached is 2 ft. in diameter. If a man exerts a force of 50 lbs. on the circumference of the wheel, how much weight can he support on the elevator?

10. A wheel with a diameter of 8 in. has firmly riveted to it two wheels of diameters 4 and 3 in., respectively. If weights of 16 and 20 lbs. are hung from these wheels, what weight must be hung from the large wheel to balance them?

11. The resistance offered by the water to the movement of the rudder of a boat is 200 lbs. The pilot wheel is 4 ft. in diameter and the axle 5 in. What force must the pilot apply to steer the boat?

12. At the top of a well there is arranged a wheel and axle. The wheel is 2 ft. in diameter. What must be the diameter of the axle for a man weighing 150 lbs. and pulling down 50 lbs. to lift himself and 100 lbs. of water out of the well?

13. The paddle wheel of a side-wheel boat is 10 ft. in diameter. If the resistance offered by the water to the movement of the wheel is 500 lbs., what force must be applied to a cog-wheel 3 ft. in diameter attached to the axle to propel the boat?

14. There is a bell 6 ft. high suspended by an axle 1 ft. from the top of the bell. Firmly attached to this axle is a wheel 6 ft. in diameter. The rope which rings the bell is attached to the circumference of the wheel. If the bell weighs 1000 lbs. and its center of gravity is 4 ft. from the top, how great a force must be applied to the rope to hold the bell in a horizontal position?

15. A boy arranges an inclined plane 20 ft. long and 5 ft. high with a wheel and axle at the top. The diameter of the wheel is 2 ft. and of the axle 8 in. He fixes a cart by a rope to the axle and by pulling on another rope which is wound around the wheel moves himself up the plane in the cart. He finds that he has to exert a force of 9 lbs. What is the resistance offered to the motion of the cart up the plane?

16. In Problem 15, how much do the boy and cart weigh?

17. In Problem 15, if the boy and cart weigh 90 lbs., with what force must the boy pull in order to move himself up the plane?

18. In Problem 15, how fast will the boy move horizontally along the ground if he pulls off 20 ft. of rope per minute?

19. The drive-wheel of a locomotive is 5 ft. in diameter. The connecting rod is attached to a pivot 8 in. from the axle. When this point of attachment is directly below the axle and a horizontal force of 1000 lbs. is exerted by the connecting rod, what will be the force that tends to move the engine in a horizontal direction?

20. On a foot lathe the rod connecting the pedal and the drive-wheel is attached 3 in. from the axle of the drive-wheel. This wheel, which is 18 in. in diameter, is belted to the 2-in. headstock of the lathe. If the pedal is moved up and down 50 times in a minute, at what rate will the block in the lathe revolve?

21. If in Problem 20 the force applied in both the up and down stroke of the pedal is 20 lbs., what weight could be lifted by a string wound around the headstock?

22. The drive-wheel of a sewing-machine is 1 ft. in diameter. The pedal crank is attached $1\frac{1}{2}$ in. from the center of the drive-wheel. The machine-wheel which is belted to the drive-wheel is 3 in. in diameter. The needle goes up and down once for every revolution of this machine-wheel. If the operator moves her feet up and down at the rate of 100 strokes a minute, how many stitches will be made per minute?

23. If in Problem 22 the stitches are $\frac{1}{12}$ of an in. long, what will be the length of the seam sewed by the movement of the operator's feet back and forth through 20 yds.?

24. A cog-wheel 1 ft. in diameter has 21 cogs on its circumference. What must be the number of cogs on the circumference of another wheel so that when geared to this its rate of motion shall be three times as fast?

25. A turn-table 20 ft. in diameter is revolved by a small wheel 3 in. in diameter cogged to its circumference. If the turn-table is to revolve once in 2 minutes, what must be the speed of the small cog-wheel?

26. The diameter of the wheel of a copying press is 14 in. The plate is lowered $\frac{1}{8}$ of an in. by every turn. If a force of 25 lbs. is applied to the wheel, what is the pressure exerted by the plate?

27. A carpenter wishes to make a bench-vise having a lever 7 in. long and a screw of such pitch that when he applies a force of 50 lbs. to the lever it will cause a pressure of 2200 lbs. on a block in the vise. How many threads must there be to the inch in the screw?

28. A mass of 1 ton is being raised by a jackscrew. If the lever of the jackscrew is 3 ft. long and the screw threads are 2 to the inch, what force must be applied to the handle to lift the weight?

29. If a screw has 5 threads to the inch, what must be the length of the lever arm for a force of 15 lbs. to produce a pressure of 5500 lbs.?

30. The wheel of an endless screw having 6 teeth to the inch, is 2 ft. in diameter and the axle 4 in. The crank arm of the screw is 14 in. long. What is the mechanical advantage of this machine?

31. The wheel at the top of a faucet is 2 in. in diameter and the screw has 8 threads to the inch. If a force of 5 lbs. is applied to the circumference of the wheel, what will be the pressure on the valve?

32. There is a fixed pulley at the bottom of a vertical wall and another at the top. A cord is passed around the pulleys, and a horse which pulls horizontally with a force of 1000 lbs. attached to it. How large a weight can the horse raise to the top of the wall?

33. A movable pulley is attached by a continuous cord to a fixed block containing two pulleys. What is the greatest weight that a force of 25 lbs. can lift?

34. There are two pulley blocks, each of which contains three pulleys. What is the greatest weight that a force of 50 lbs. can be made to lift with them?

35. In Problem 34, what would be the tension on the rope?

36. What is the least number of pulleys, both fixed and movable, that are necessary to enable a force of 16 lbs. to lift a weight of 144 lbs.?

37. A man who can exert a force of 100 lbs. has two blocks of pulleys, one containing three and the other two pulleys. What is the greatest weight he can lift?

38. If a force of 100 lbs. is able by the use of two blocks of pulleys to lift a weight of $\frac{1}{2}$ a ton, how many pulleys must there be in each block?

39. On a derrick there is a crank, the arm of which is 2 ft. long, which is attached to a cylinder 8 in. in diameter.

The rope which winds about this cylinder is passed around two blocks of three pulleys each, one of which is fixed and the other movable. With a force of 100 lbs. applied to the crank, what weight can be lifted ?

40. A man weighing 150 lbs. has a rope and two simple pulleys. What is the least muscular force that he can exert to hold himself suspended from a beam by means of these appliances?

41. A spring balance suspended from the ceiling of a room has a pulley attached to it. Another spring balance is placed directly below the first and its ring fastened to the floor. A cord is attached to the hook of the second spring balance and the free end passed over the pulley. A 10-lb. weight is fastened to the free end of the cord. What is the reading on each spring balance and the tension on the string? Neglect the weights of the balance and pulley.

42. If the area of the end of the large piston of a hydraulic press is 2 sq. m. and the area of the small piston 1½ sq. cm., what force must be applied to the small piston to produce a pressure of 100 kgm. ?

43. In Problem 42, if the small piston moves through a distance of 6 cm., how far will the large piston move ?

44. The pistons of a hydrostatic press are circular and have diameters of 3 in. and 3 ft., respectively. The smaller piston is worked by a lever the arms of which are 2 and 10 in. If a force of 100 lbs. is applied to the end of the lever, what weight can be supported on the larger piston ?

45. A uniformly tapering wedge 12 in. long and 2 in. thick at the base is shoved with a force of 100 lbs. between two cakes of ice. What is the force tending to push the cakes apart ?

46. In using an air-pump it is found that the power applied to the pump handle goes through 8 times the distance the piston rises. If the area of the piston is $\frac{1}{2}$ sq. cm. and the barometer stands at 76 cm., what power must be applied to work the pump when the density of the air inside the bell jar is $\frac{1}{2}$ what it is outside?

47. In a suction pump the distance from the pivot to the point where the hand is applied is 20 in. and to the piston rod is 2 in. If the diameter of the piston is 4 in., what force must be applied to the handle to raise water from a well 20 ft. deep? Barometer is 30 in?

48. There is a door 2 in. thick and $2\frac{1}{2}$ ft. wide. The hinges are flush with the surface of the door. A man gets his finger between the casing and the door on the hinge edge of the door. If a force of 5 lbs. is acting at right angles to the surface of the door at the free edge, with what force is his finger jammed?

49. In a wheelbarrow the distance between the axle of the wheel and the point of application of the hands to the handle-bars is 5 ft. If 75 lbs. of coal are placed in the barrow so that its center of gravity is $1\frac{1}{2}$ ft. from the axis of the wheel, and the floor of the barrow is held horizontal, what will be the pressure of the wheel on the ground? Disregard the weight of the barrow.

50. In Problem 49, if the barrow weighs 25 lbs. and its weight centers at the same point as the coal, what horizontal force must be exerted to push the barrow along? The coefficient of friction of the wheel with the ground is $\frac{1}{10}$.

LIGHT

1. The nearest fixed star is 19,000,000,000 miles from the earth. How long does it take light to come from this star to the earth?

2. What must be the relative areas of two planes in order that they may intercept the same amount of light from a luminous point, if one plane is 3 times as far as the other from the point?

3. If the diameter of the earth were twice as great, how much more of the sun's light would the earth intercept than it now does?

4. What part of the light given out by a lamp does a board 1 ft. square and 50 ft. distant from the lamp receive?

5. If the sun is 93,000,000 miles away, and the diameter of the earth is 8000 miles, how much of the light given off by the sun strikes the earth?

6. A body situated 100 ft. from a luminous point is moved 20 ft. nearer to the point. How much more light does it intercept than before?

7. The areas of two plane surfaces are to each other as 2 : 6. What will be the ratio of their distances from a luminous point if each of them intercepts the same amount of light?

8. In determining the illuminating power of a lamp by a Bunsen photometer the distance from the lamp to the screen was 100 cm. and from the screen to the candle 30 cm. What was the candle power of the lamp?

9. How many candles will be required to produce the same intensity of illumination at 2 m. distance that is produced by 1 candle at 30 cm. distance?

10. How many candles must be placed 100 cm. from a screen in order to illuminate it as much as two candles placed 12 cm. from the screen?

11. Two lights are distant from a screen 80 ft. and 12 ft. If the intensities of their illuminations of the screen are as

2 : 3, respectively, what are the relative intensities of the two lights ?

12. An 8-candle power lamp and a candle are placed 5 m. apart. How far from the lamp in a straight line joining the flames must a screen be placed that it may be equally illuminated by each of them?

13. The candle powers of two lamps are to each other as 3 : 4 and their distances from a screen as 2 : 3. What are the relative intensities of their illumination of the screen ?

14. The diameters of two spherical bodies are to each other as 2 . 3 and their distances from a luminous point as 3 : 4. What is the relative amount of light intercepted by each ?

15. An 8-candle power lamp is 10 ft. away from a standard candle. On a straight line which is of indefinite length and passes through the lamp and candle, select two points at either of which a screen will be equally illuminated by lamp and candle.

16. Two lights whose candle powers are 5 and 7 are placed 10 ft. apart. At what point between them must a screen be placed that the intensity of illumination of the side toward the 5-candle power light may be twice as great as that of the opposite side ?

17. The intensities of two lights are as 4 · 9 and their distance apart is 20 ft. How far from the weaker light and on a line joining them must a screen be placed to be equally illuminated on each side?

18. The diameter of the moon is about 2160 miles and of the earth 8000 miles. The distance from the sun to the earth is 93,000,000 miles, and from the moon to the earth 240,000 miles. What is the greatest tangential flat area on the earth which can be covered by a total eclipse of the sun?

19. Using the data of the previous problem, what part approximately of the light emitted by the sun, considering the moon as a perfect reflector, reaches the earth on a night when the moon is full ?

20. What is the length of the shadow of a tree 50 ft. tall when the sun is 45° above the horizon ?

21. What is the height of a tree which casts a shadow 100 ft. long when a rod 5 ft. high casts a shadow 7 ft. long ?

22. A tree stands on the margin of a pool which is 30 ft. wide. On the ground 5 ft. back of the opposite margin of the pool stands a person whose eye is 5 ft. above the level of the pool. In this position the person can see the image of the tree just touching his margin of the pool. How high is the tree ?

23. The image of a stake 8 ft. long and 10 ft. from a shutter is seen on a screen 4 ft. from the shutter. The aperture in the shutter through which the light from the stake passes is minute. What is the size of the image ?

24. The floor of a room 20 ft. wide and 10 ft. high is 2 ft. below the level of the surrounding ground. Through a small hole in the center of the side of the room the image of a man 6 ft. tall and standing at a distance of 25 ft. from the hole is thrown upon the opposite wall. How far from the floor will the head of the man appear?

25. What is the greatest angle at which the light from an object can strike a plane mirror and form an image ?

26. The clock on a wall indicates 9.30. What time will it appear to indicate to a person seeing the reflection of the clock in a mirror on the opposite wall but too far away to see the figures distinctly?

27. A plane mirror lies upon a table and a pencil 6 in. long stands on one of the edges of the mirror. How long

must the mirror be that the entire pencil may be seen reflected in it by a person whose eyes are 10 in. horizontally
from the edge of the mirror next him and 5 in. above the
table?

28. A man standing in front of a mirror closes one eye
and then places upon the mirror a piece of paper just large
enough to cover the image of the closed eye from the sight
of the open eye. He then closes his open eye and opens
the other. Will he now be able to see the image of the
closed eye?

29. A square plane mirror hangs in the center of one of
the walls of a cubical room. What must be the size of the
mirror that an observer with his eye in the center of the
room may see the whole of the opposite wall reflected in it?
[Deschanel.]

30. Prove that if an object is placed in front of a plane
mirror and the mirror is moved parallel to itself, either
toward or from the object, the image will move twice as far
as the mirror.

31. A lamp is placed at the bottom of a vertical wall, and
a plane mirror is to be placed at the top of the wall in such
a position as to reflect the light from the lamp horizontally.
What angle will the mirror make with the horizon?

32. Show by a drawing that a man cannot see himself at
full length in a vertical mirror unless the mirror is at least
$\frac{1}{2}$ as long as he.

33. Prove that if a candle is placed in front of a vertical
plane mirror and the mirror revolved 45° about a vertical
axis the image will move through an arc of 90°.

34. A line 3 ft. long is drawn across a table; and a mirror 4 in. long is placed with the center of its back over the
center of the line, the surface being parallel to the line and

at right angles to the surface of the table; 5 in. from the end of the line and 3 in. from the line on the side facing the mirror a candle is placed. Will there be an image of the candle formed, and if so, where ?

35. Two plane mirrors facing and parallel to each other are 6 cm. apart. An object is placed 2 cm. from one of the mirrors and between them. Calculate the distance from the mirror (*a*) of the third image ; (*b*) of the fifth image.

36. Show by a drawing the position of the images formed of an object placed midway between two plane mirrors whose surfaces make an angle of 45° with each other.

37. Two plane mirrors are placed at an angle of 45° to each other, and a candle is placed at a perpendicular distance of 10 cm. in front of each. At what distance back of the mirrors will the images appear after three reflections ?

38. Show that the images formed by the third reflection of an object in each of two plane mirrors placed at an angle of 60° with each other lie at a common point back of the mirrors.

39. At what angle with each other must two plane mirrors be placed that there may be formed eleven images of an object which is 5 cm. from each mirror?

40. If the earth were a perfect sphere 8000 miles in diameter, how far away from a man at sea whose eyes are 15 ft. above the level of the water will the horizon be as seen by him ?

41. A picture 10 ft. square hangs on a wall. How small a mirror on the opposite wall 20 ft. away, the center of which is directly opposite the center of the picture, will reflect an image of the picture entire to a man whose eye is halfway between the picture and the mirror and on a level with their centers ?

42. The minute spaces on the dial of a clock are 1 in. apart, and the hands are 2 in. from the face of the dial. When it is just 12 o'clock, it appears to be 2 minutes past 12 to a person standing at a certain position in front of the clock. When he walks 100 ft. from his first position in a direction parallel to the face of the clock, the time appears to be 3 minutes before 12. If the circular arrangement of the spaces on the dial is not considered, what is the distance of the person from the clock? Neglect time required to walk 100 ft.

43. The radius of curvature of a concave mirror is 30 cm. How far from the mirror on the principal axis will the image of an object which is 50 cm. from the mirror appear?

44. If the radius of curvature of a concave mirror is 50 cm and a candle is placed 40 cm. from the mirror, where will its image appear?

45. An arrow 6 in. long is placed 20 in. in front of a concave mirror whose radius of curvature is 2 ft. Where will the image appear and what will be its length?

46. In the previous problem, how long will the image be (*a*) if the object is 5 ft. in front of the mirror? (*b*) if it is 2 in. in front of the mirror?

47. What is the focal length of a concave mirror whose radius of curvature is 18 in.? Where will the image of a candle placed at the center of curvature appear?

48. What kind of an image will be formed by the mirror of the preceding problem if the object is placed 25 in. from the mirror? How large an image?

49. A real image formed by a concave mirror, the focal length of which is 20 cm., is twice as large as the object. Where are the object and image situated?

50. An image produced by a concave mirror is 8 times as large as the object. If the focal length of the mirror is 10 in., where are the object and image situated?

51. A man stands with his eye exactly at the center of curvature of a concave spherical mirror. How many images of himself can he see?

52. When a candle is placed on the principal axis of a concave spherical mirror 50 cm. from the mirror, a real and inverted image is formed on a screen held at a greater distance from the mirror than the candle. If the image is 3 times as large as the object, what is the focal length of the mirror?

53. An object is placed 45 cm. in front of a concave spherical mirror the radius of curvature of which is 80 cm. What change will be made in the size and position of the image if the object is moved 10 cm. nearer the mirror?

54. A candle placed in the axis of a concave spherical mirror 20 cm. from the mirror shows a real image 50 cm. from the mirror. What is the radius of curvature of the mirror?

55. Prove that the image formed by a convex mirror is always smaller than the object.

56. If an object is placed in front of a convex mirror and at a distance equal to the focal length of the mirror, what will be the relative size of image and object?

57. If an object is placed at a distance in front of a convex mirror equal to the radius of curvature of the mirror, (a) where will the image be? (b) of what size?

58. An object is placed 10 cm. in front of a convex mirror the radius of curvature of which is 30 cm. (a) Where is the image? (b) Of what size?

59. If in the previous problem the object had been placed 20 cm. from the mirror, where would the image have appeared?

60. In Problem 58, what would have been (*a*) the position of the image if the object had been placed 40 cm. from the mirror? (*b*) the size?

61. Show by a diagram the refraction between two media when the angle of incidence is (*a*) 60° and the angle of refraction is 30°; (*b*) 45° and 20°. In each case, which is the denser medium?

62. If the critical angle of a certain substance is 60°, what is the index of refraction?

63. If the index of refraction for diamond is 2.5, what is the critical angle?

64. If the index of refraction for two media is ¾, at what angle will a ray incident at 60° be refracted in passing from the denser to the rarer medium?

65. There is a glass prism the faces of which make angles of 60° with each other. What angle must a ray of light make with one of these faces to receive the least possible refraction?

66. The critical angle of a certain medium is 45°. A ray of light passing through this medium makes an angle of 30° with a perpendicular to the surface. What angle will it make with the perpendicular after emerging from the medium?

67. A prism has angles which are each 60° and its index of refraction is 2. A ray of light enters the prism at an angle of 45° with one of its faces. What is the angle which the emergent ray forms with the opposite face?

68. Show that the image formed by a convex lens may be either larger or smaller than the object.

69. Prove that, when the distance of an object from a convex lens is twice the focal length, the image is ·at the same distance on the other side.

70. Plot the image of an object placed inside the principal focus of a double convex lens.

71. A rod 5 cm. long held in front of a convex lens forms an image 25 cm. long upon a screen 100 cm. from the lens. What is the focal length of the lens?

72. A convex lens 10 ft. from a screen throws a distinct image of a certain object on the screen. If the image is 5 times as large as the object, (a) what is the focal length of the lens? (b) what is the distance of the object from it?

73. A lamp is placed 12 ft. from a screen, and it is found that when a convex lens is placed 3 ft. from the lamp a sharp image of the lamp is thrown upon the screen. What is the focal length of the lens?

74. An object 4 cm. long is placed 20 cm. from a lens, and a real image is formed 10 cm. from the lens. If the object is placed 10 cm. from the lens, (a) where will the image be? (b) how large?

75. The lens in a camera has a focal length of 15 in. How far from the lens must an object be in order that a clearly defined image of it may be thrown on a sensitive plate which is 16 in. from the lens?

76. At what distance from a convex lens of focal length F must an object be placed that the image may be $\frac{1}{4}$ as large as the object?

77. A wafer 1 cm. in diameter is held 10 cm. from a convex lens and on its principal axis. If the focal length of the lens is 50 cm., find the position and size of the image.

78. With a convex lens of 15 cm. focal length, where must the object be placed to form an image 4 times as large as the object (a) for a real image? (b) for a virtual?

79. If a 10-cent piece is 18 mm. in diameter and a silver dollar 38 mm. in diameter, at what distance in front of a

convex lens whose focal length is 10 cm. must the 10-cent piece be placed to form an image as large as the silver dollar?

80. Where must an object be placed to form a real image 10 ft. away from a convex lens the focal length of which is 1 ft.?

81. The conjugate foci of a lens are 20 and 30 cm. distant from the lens on opposite sides. How far from the lens would the rays of the sun be focused?

82. If when an object is placed 4 in. from a common magnifying glass it appears to be magnified 4 times, what is the focal length of the magnifying glass?

83. Prove by means of a diagram that an object of appreciable size placed farther than the focal length in front of a convex lens of equally curved surfaces will form an image concave toward the lens.

84. Prove that if the object in the previous problem is placed between the principal focus and the lens, the image will be convex toward the lens.

85. Deduce the facts proved in the previous problems concerning the curvature of the image from the equations $\dfrac{1}{D_0} + \dfrac{1}{D_1} = \dfrac{1}{F}$ and $\dfrac{1}{D_0} - \dfrac{1}{D_1} = \dfrac{1}{F}$.

86. An object is placed 10 cm. in front of a convex lens the focal length of which is 6 cm. If now the object is moved 1 cm. nearer the lens, what will be the distance traveled by the image?

87. A convex lens the focal length of which is 2 ft. is to be used to throw a picture on a screen 20 ft. from the lens. How far from the lens must the glass slide be placed?

88. Two of the conjugate foci of a convex lens are 10 and 15 cm. respectively from the lens. If owing to a change in the lens the conjugate foci become 8 and 20 cm. from the lens, how has the focal length of the lens been affected?

SOUND

Velocity of sound at o° C. = 332 m per second.   Increase = 6o cm. per 1° C.

Velocity of sound at o° C. = 1090 ft. per second.   Increase = 2 ft. per 1° C.

1. What time will be required for sound to travel 1 mile (*a*) when the temperature is o° C. ? (*b*) when the temperature is 40° C. ?

2. The Eiffel Tower is 1000 ft. high.   A man stands on the ground 500 yds. from the center of the base of the tower. If the man's height is neglected, how long after a sound is made at the top of the tower will he hear it?   The temperature is 20° C.

3. A church bell is ringing at a distance of ¼ mile from one listener and ⅓ mile from a second.   How much louder does it sound to the first than to the second man?

4. On a day when the thermometer is at o° C. a man riding in a railway train, which moves at the rate of 1 mile a minute, hears a clock directly ahead of him strike with an interval of 1 second between the strokes.   What was the actual time between the strokes?

5. On a day when the thermometer stands at 15° C. a stone is dropped from the top of a vertical cliff.   The sound caused by its striking the bottom of the cliff reaches a person on the top just 8 seconds after the stone was dropped. What is the height of the cliff?

6. A bullet fired with a velocity of 1200 ft. per second is heard to strike a target 5 seconds after it left the rifle. What is the distance of the target, the temperature being 15° C.?

7. A man, wishing to know the air-line distance between his house and a town, observed that on a day when the thermometer was $-20°$ C. it took 1 second more for the sound of a whistle in the town to reach him than it did on a day when the thermometer stood at 20° C. What is the distance?

8. On a day when the thermometer stands at 20° C. two reports are made with an intermission of 2 seconds between them. With what velocity must a man be moving away from the point where the reports originated to cause them to reach him with an interval of 3 seconds between them?

9. On a day when the thermometer stands at 13° C. a person riding on a train moving with a velocity of a mile a minute hears a bell directly ahead which seems to produce a note similar to that produced by a tuning fork making 320 vibrations per second. What is the number of vibrations made by the bell?

10. A tuning fork which is known to make 300 vibrations per second is thrown into vibration and placed near another fork which seems to produce the same note. Two beats per second are noticed. What is the rate of vibration of the second fork?

11. What effect will a rise of 20° C. have upon the wave length produced by a tuning fork making 480 vibrations per second?

12. If a tuning fork vibrates 374 times per second, what is the length of its resonance tube on a day when the thermometer stands at $-10°$ C.?

13. What will be the length of the waves given off by a C, 262 vibrations, tuning fork on a day when the temperature is 20° C.?

14. If on a day when the temperature is 10° C. a tube 15 in. long gives the best resonance for a tuning fork, what is the vibration number of the fork?

15. A smoked-glass plate is placed vertically in front of a vibrating fork provided with a style. The plate is free to fall under the influence of gravity, and 120 waves are found to be inserted on the plate by the style in the first foot of its length. Determine the vibration number of the fork.

16. What is the length of an open pipe that at 70° F. gives the note C, 262 vibrations?

17. What is the length of a closed pipe which at 60° F. produces the note G, 392 vibrations?

18. What is the length of a closed tube which at 0° C. will give the greatest reinforcement to the sound of a tuning fork making 256 vibrations per second?

19. What is the length of an open tube that will produce the maximum resonance at 20° C., when a vibrating tuning fork which makes 384 vibrations per second is held near one end?

20. An open pipe which ought to respond to the note E, 330 vibrations, was found to respond to the note F, 350 vibrations. To remedy this, ⅙ of its length was cut off and a cap put on one of the ends. To what number of vibrations will it now respond?

21. If the G string of a violin is shortened ⅙, what note will be produced when it is thrown into vibration?

22. If the E string of a violin is 15 in. long, how much must it be shortened to produce the note E♯?

23. If the thickness of a wire is doubled, the length halved, and the tension trebled, what effect will this have upon the number of vibrations it will make in a given time?

24. A wire 3 ft. long and .2 mm. in diameter, when stretched with a force of 10 lbs., makes 260 vibrations per second upon being thrown into vibration. How many vibrations per second will be made by a wire of the same material 2 ft. long and .1 mm. in diameter if stretched by a force of 4 lbs. ?

25. There are two wires of the same material and the same length, but one of them is twice as thick as the other. How much greater force must be applied to the larger wire to cause it to produce when vibrated the same note as the smaller wire produces?

26. A certain cord when stretched by a force of 25 lbs. is found to make 254 vibrations per second. How much must the force be increased to cause it to make 275 vibrations per second?

27. If a vibrating string is found to produce the note C when stretched by a force of 10 lbs., what must be the force exerted to cause it to produce (*a*) the note E? (*b*) the note G?

HEAT

1. Reduce 8°, 20°, 70°, — 40°, and 10° C. to the Fahrenheit scale.

2. Reduce 8°, 40°, 180°, — 10°, and 36° F. to the Centigrade scale.

3. What must be the temperature of a liquid so that both the Fahrenheit and Centigrade thermometers shall read the same when immersed in it?

4. Absolute zero is 273° below zero on the Centigrade scale. What is this temperature on the Fahrenheit scale?

5. Iron melts at 1200° C. What is the melting point on the Fahrenheit scale?

6. The average difference in temperature between two places is 60° F. How much would this be on the Centigrade scale?

7. Lead expands .000028 of its length for every degree Centigrade. How much would it expand for a degree Fahrenheit?

8 The coefficient of linear expansion of iron is .000011. How much must an iron rod 40 ft. long be heated to expand 1 in.?

9. At 20° C. a steel meter rod is found to be 100.01654 cm. long. At what temperature will it be correct?

10. The brass pendulum of a clock is 1 m. long when the temperature is 10° C. (a) What will be its length at 0° C.? (b) at 25° C.?

11. A wire 10 ft. long at 0° C., heated 90°, increases its length .31 in. What is its coefficient of linear expansion?

12. An iron rod 250 cm. long at 10° C. is .09 cm. longer at 40° C. What will be its length at 60° C.?

13. How much room must a steel pipe 100 ft. long at 20° C. have left for expansion if its maximum temperature is to be 100° C.?

14. A brass rod is 1 m. long at 0° C. How long will it be at 75° C.?

15. An iron rod is 105.4 cm. long at 100° C. What is its length at 0° C.?

16. A rod 10 m. long is found to have expanded .95 cm. when heated from 0° to 50° C. What part of its length at 60° C. would it expand if heated from 60° to 70° F.?

17. The barometer at 0° C. stands at 750 mm. At what height will it stand if the temperature rises to 30° C., the pressure remaining the same? Disregard the expansion of the glass and scale.

18. The steel rails in a certain road are 30 ft. long at 0° C., and the difference between the extremes of summer and

winter temperature is 117° F. What will be the difference in length of the rails between these two temperatures?

19. On a day when the temperature of the air is 25° C., a 40-yd. track is measured off with a 10-ft. steel tape correct at 0° C. What will be the error in the length of the track?

20. What is the length of a steel rod which increases 1 in. when heated 200° C.?

21. A brass tape 30 m. in length at 0° C. was graduated to $\frac{1}{100}$ of a cm. When the thermometer was 30° C. it was used to measure a kilometer. How much was the error in measurement?

22. A steel locomotive driving-wheel is 6 ft. in diameter at 0° C. How much farther will it go per revolution when its temperature is 25° C.?

23. Two rods, one of zinc and the other of platinum, which at zero measure exactly 1 m. each, are heated to 90° C. What part of the length of the platinum rod at 90° C. will be the gain in length of the zinc rod?

24. Two rods, each 2 m. long at 0° C., one brass and the other iron, are laid side by side and joined at one end. Will there be any difference in their lengths when heated to 25° C.? If so, how much?

25. A platinum rod and a brass rod each measure 1 m. at 0° C. How much must they be heated in order to have the brass rod 2 mm. longer than the platinum rod?

26. If at 0° C. an iron rod measures 201 cm. and a brass rod 200 cm., to what temperature must they be raised to be of the same length? What will their common length be?

27. If a 4-m. brass wire stretches 1 cm. with a force of 2 kgm., how much weight could be lifted by cooling this wire from 120° C. to 0° C.?

28. In a linear expansion apparatus of the lever form the long arm of the pointer is 36 cm. long, and the short arm .4 cm. The pointer rises 5.4 cm. when a rod in the apparatus is raised from 25° C. to 100° C. What is the coefficient of linear expansion of the rod if its length is 75 cm.?

29. Find the coefficient of linear expansion of a rod from the following data taken from an experiment with the expansion apparatus :

Length of rod	60 cm
Length of long arm of lever	24 "
Length of short arm of lever	2.5 "
Height of long arm on scale before heating .	5 "
Height of long arm on scale after heating . .	5 48 "
Temperature of rod before heating . .	20° C.
Temperature of rod after heating	100° C.

30. A plate-glass window is 10 ft. by 12 ft. How much will it change in area if its temperature changes from 0° C. to 25° C.?

31. An iron rod 1.001 cm. in diameter of cross-section at 0° C. is to have a brass ring, which at the same temperature is 1 cm. in internal diameter, shrunk to it. To what temperature must they both be heated that the ring may be placed on the rod?

32. A glass liter flask is filled with mercury at 0° C. and then heated to 100° C. How much mercury runs out? Disregard the expansion of flask.

33. The sp. gr. of mercury at 0° C. is 13.6. What is it at 300° C.?

34. How much mercury must be below the zero point of a Centigrade thermometer when plunged into a freezing mixture, if the diameter of the tube is $\frac{1}{200}$ of a mm., in order that the length of a degree may be 2 mm.? Disregard the expansion of the glass.

35. A cubical block of gold was found at 0° C. to contain 8000 c.c. What will be the contents at 100° C.? How much more will it weigh?

36. An aluminum cylinder is 10 cm. long and 3 cm. in diameter measured at 0° C. (*a*) What is its volume at 100° C.? (*b*) If its density is 2.7 at the lower temperature, what is it at the higher?

37. A glass beaker measures 10 cm. deep and 5 cm. in diameter at 0° C. How much water will it hold at 100° C.? Disregard the expansion of the water.

38. A liter flask is correct in cubical contents at 0° C., and the density of mercury is 13.6 g. per c.c. at 0° C. How many grams of mercury will the flask hold at 50° C.?

39. A cubical box of copper 10 cm. on a side is filled with mercury, and then heated until 1 c.c. of mercury runs out. How many degrees Centigrade is its temperature raised?

40. How much longer must an iron rod be than one of copper in order that the two may expand the same amount for every degree C.?

41. A solid glass globe 10 cm. in diameter when measured at 0° C., and weighing 1800 g., was placed in water and the temperature raised to 100° C. Supposing that the sp. gr. of the water remains 1, what will be the apparent weight of the globe when thus immersed?

42. There is a zinc rod 5 m. long and 20 cm. square at 0° C., which is to be covered by a coating 1 mm. thick. How many more sq. mm. of coating will be required when the temperature is 30° C. than when it is 0° C.?

43. When 200 g. of brass at 100° C. are turned into 100 g. of water at 40.5° C., the temperature of the water is raised to 50° C. What is the specific heat of brass?

44. Five hundred g. of a certain substance at 100° C. are poured into 140 g. of water at 20° C., raising its temperature to 40° C. What is the sp. ht. of the substance?

45. Ten g. of iron at 100° C. are plunged into 9 g. of water at 10° C., raising the temperature of the water thereby to 20° C. What is the sp. ht. of the iron?

46. Ten g. of nickel are heated to 100° C., and placed in 5 g. of water at 0° C. What is the resulting temperature?

47. How much brass at 100° C. must be turned into 20 g. of snow at 0° C. to melt the snow and raise the temperature to 40° C.?

48. How much heat will it take to raise 20 g. of silver from 0° C. to 60° C.?

49. How much heat will be given out by 8 g. of zinc in cooling from 75° to 5° C.?

50. Fifty g. of copper at 100° C. are plunged into 100 g. of water at 0° C. What will be the resulting temperature?

51. One hundred g. of lead at 100° C. are put into 200 g. of alcohol at 0° C. What will be the resulting temperature?

52. One hundred g. of water at 80° C. are thoroughly mixed with 500 g. of mercury at 0° C. What is the temperature of the mixture?

53. How much ether at 30° C. must be mixed with 10 g. of water at 6° C. that the resulting temperature may be 10° C.?

54. A pound of sulphur at 0° C. is placed in a pound of water at 122° F. What will be the resulting temperature?

55. Fifty g. of mercury at 100° C. are mixed with 50 g. of water at 0° C. What is the resulting temperature?

56. How much mercury at 100° C. must be mixed with 40 g. of water at 10° C. that the resulting temperature may be 25° C.?

57. A rod composed of platinum and silver and weighing 16 g. is heated to 100° C., and dropped into 10 g. of water at 14° C., the temperature of the water being raised thereby to 20° C. How much platinum in the rod?

58. How much tin at 100° C. must be put into 100 g. of mercury at 10° C. to raise the temperature to 20° C.?

59. One hundred g. of lead at 0° C. are placed in 50 g. of water at 212° F. The water is found to lose 2° C. when the lead is taken out. How much has the temperature of the lead increased?

60. A bar of iron weighing 5 lbs. at 0° C. is placed in 2 lbs. of water at 100° C., and after remaining for a few minutes is taken out, when its temperature is found to have risen to 40° C. What is the temperature of the water?

61. Find the latent heat of melting ice from the following data:

Weight of calorimeter	60 g.
Weight of calorimeter and water	460 g.
Temperature of water	38° C.
Temperature of the mixture	5° C.
Weight of calorimeter, water, and ice . .	618 g.
Specific heat of calorimeter	.1

62. Find the latent heat of melting ice from the following data:

Weight of calorimeter	80 g.
Weight of calorimeter and alcohol	530 g.
Temperature of alcohol	30° C
Temperature of the mixture . . .	8° C.
Weight of the calorimeter, alcohol, and ice . .	604 g.
Specific heat of alcohol	64
Specific heat of calorimeter	.1
No chemical action	

63. How much heat will it take to change 6 g. of ice at 0° C. to water at 40° C.?

64. On a cold night in the winter a farmer fills a cubical tank in his cellar with water. In the morning he finds that the water has just begun to freeze. How much heat has been given out to the cellar? The tank is ½ m. on a side. The temperature of the water when put in was 70° C.

65. Just what will occur if 1000 calories be applied to 20 g. of ice at 0° C.?

66. How many inches of rain at 4° F. must fall in order to melt ½ in. of ice at 0° C.?

67. How much heat will it take to melt a mass of 10 g. of zinc taken at 0° C.?

68. How much heat will be used in raising 50 g. of iron from 0° C. to the melting point and just melting it?

69. How much water at 100° C. must be mixed with 10 g. of ice at − 10° C. that the resulting temperature may be 10° C.?

70. How many grams of iron at 90° C. will be required to change 8 g. of ice at 0° C. into water at 25° C.?

71. Fifty g. of melted tin at 235° C. are poured into 40 g. of water at 0° C. What will be the resulting temperature?

72. Four hundred g. of melted lead at 330° C. are turned into 50 g. of ice at 0° C. What will be the result if there is no loss of heat by radiation?

73. Assume that mixing has no effect on the thermal capacities of oil of turpentine and alcohol What will be the resulting temperature if 5 g. of ice at 0° C. are dropped into a 10-g. mixture of equal parts of these substances at 70° C.?

74. Ten lbs. of zinc at 80° C. are turned into a pound mixture of snow and water, raising the temperature thereby to 20° C. How much snow in the mixture?

75. Into a 1 lb. mixture of snow and water are turned 2 lbs. of water at 29° C. The resulting temperature is found to be 2° C. How much snow was in the mixture?

76. How much melted zinc at 420° C. must be poured into 100 g. of mercury at 0° C. to raise its temperature to 80° C.?

77. Find the latent heat of vaporization of steam from the following data:

Weight of calorimeter	300 g.
Weight of calorimeter and water	. 750 g.
Weight of calorimeter, water, and steam	790 25 g.
Temperature of the water .	. . 6° C
Temperature of the steam	. 100° C.
Temperature of the mixture . .	. . 55° C
Specific heat of calorimeter	. .1

78. Find the latent heat of vaporization of steam from the following data:

Weight of calorimeter	200 g.
Weight of calorimeter and turpentine	. 820 g.
Temperature of turpentine	4° C.
Temperature of the mixture	. . 32° C.
Temperature of the steam . .	100° C.
Weight of calorimeter, turpentine, and steam .	834.4 g.
Specific heat of turpentine . . .	.47
Specific heat of calorimeter .	. .1

79. Eight g. of steam at 200° C. are cooled to 0° C. How much heat is given out?

80. Ten g. of steam at 100° C. are cooled to 41° F. How much heat is given out?

81. One lb. of water at 10° C. is the result of cooling the same mass of steam from 110° C. How much snow at — 10° C. would be melted by the heat thus given out?

82. How many calories of heat will be needed to change 8 g. of ice at — 40° F. to steam at 500° F.?

83. Four g. of ice at $-10°$ C. are changed into steam at $200°$ C. How much heat is used?

84. How much heat will it take to melt 5 g. of ice at $0°$ C. and change it into steam at $100°$ C.?

85. How many grams of ice at $-10°$ C. will be turned into water at $50°$ C. by 10 g. of steam at $200°$ C.?

86. How much heat would be required to change 20 g. of ice at $-15°$ C. to steam at $765°$ C.? The pressure of the steam is constant.

87. One hundred g. of steam at atmospheric pressure are condensed by passing into a 500-g. mixture of ice and water at $0°$ C. The final temperature is $70°$ C. How many grams of ice were there in the mixture?

88. How many units of heat will be required to evaporate 6 g. of alcohol at $0°$ C.?

89. A 500-g. mass of iron and copper turnings, taken in equal parts and at a temperature of $1000°$ C., is put into 100 g. of alcohol at $-10°$ C. What is the result? Specific heat of alcohol vapor is .45.

90. How much liquid lead at $330°$ C. must be put into 10 g. of oil of turpentine at $10°$ C. to evaporate it?

91. How much melted zinc at $433°$ C. must be placed in 20 g. of alcohol at $0°$ C. to evaporate it?

92. How much heat will be given off by 100 g. of sulphur vapor in cooling from $440°$ C. to $10°$ C.?

93. How much melted tin at $230°$ C. must be poured into 10 g. of oil of turpentine at $10°$ C. to evaporate it?

94. To how many ft. lbs. of energy are 8 calories of heat equivalent?

95. An iron anvil weighing 100 lbs. is struck by a hammer weighing 10 lbs., and moving at the rate of 30 ft. per second. If all the energy is used in heating the anvil, how many degrees is its temperature raised?

96. On a day when the temperature is 20° C., 5 cu. ft. of water at 20° C. are poured from a certain height into 10 cu. ft. of water at 0° C. The temperature of the water after mixing is found to be 7° C. From what height did the water fall? A cu. ft. of water weighs 62.5 lbs. No energy was lost.

97. How far above the surface of the earth must a cake of ice be carried to be melted by the impact of its fall, if all the energy is changed into heat?

98. A body weighing 10 kg. and moving along the ice with a velocity of 5 m. per second is stopped by the friction of the surface. If all the energy is changed into heat, which acts upon the surface of the ice, how much ice is melted?

99. How many inches of rain at 10° C. must fall to melt ½ in. of ice at 0° C.? Consider the sp. gr. of ice 1.

100. How many inches of rain at 10° C. must fall to melt ½ in. of ice at 0° C.? Consider the sp. gr. of ice .9.

EXPANSION AND CONTRACTION OF GASES

1. A sealed tube filled with air at 0° C. and 76 cm. pressure is able to withstand a pressure of 10 lbs. to the sq. in. If this tube is placed in the receiver of an air-pump from which the air is gradually exhausted, what will be the height of a barometer placed in the same receiver at the instant the tube breaks?

2. A barometer in the receiver of an air-pump stands at 10 in. If the piston of the pump has an area of 2 sq. in., how much force will be needed to lift it? The atmospheric pressure is equal to a pressure of 30 in. of mercury.

3. A cu. dm. of gas weighs 6 g. when the barometer stands at 76 cm. Other conditions remaining the same, under what pressure will a cu. dm. of this gas weigh 8 g.?

4. Mercury is poured into the open arm of a Mariotte's tube until the air in the closed arm is decreased $\frac{2}{3}$. What is now the difference in heights of the mercury columns? The barometer stands at 74 cm.   •

5. A tube 2 m. long, closed at one end, is filled with air and plunged open end down into a cistern of mercury until the volume of the air is decreased $\frac{1}{4}$ How far is the lower end of the tube below the surface of the mercury in the cistern?

6. An open tube 50 cm. long is plunged to a depth of 40 cm. in a cistern of mercury, and then the upper end is closed. If the tube is now lifted so that this end is 20 cm. above the level of the mercury in the cistern, what will be the difference of level between the mercury in the tube and that in the cistern?

7. Owing to the pressure of air in the space above the mercury column in a barometer tube 85 cm. long, it is found to indicate a pressure of 70 cm., when an accurate barometer indicates a pressure of 76 cm. What will be the pressure indicated by this barometer when the accurate barometer stands at 72?

8. A gas at constant pressure expands $\frac{1}{273}$ of its volume at 0° C. for every degree it is raised above 0° C. How much will it expand for every degree F. above 32° F.?

9. An open vessel was heated until $\frac{1}{3}$ the air it contained at 0° C. was driven out. How much was it heated?

10. How much must a liter of air at 10° C. be heated in order to increase its volume $\frac{2}{3}$?

11. A gas at 0° C. and 760 mm. pressure measured 250 c.c. What will it measure at − 10° C. and 750 mm. pressure?

12. A volume of gas measured 1 cu. ft. at − 4° F. and 30 in. pressure. What will be its volume at 68° F. and 39.4 in. pressure?

13. A flask holding 600 c.c. of air at 0° C. is heated to 25° C. What volume of expanded air escapes? Temperature of escaped air equals 25° C. Neglect expansion of flask.

14. A liter flask filled with air at − 10° C. is heated to 70° C. What will be the volume of the air that escapes if measured at 0° C.?

15. A vessel full of air at 0° C. is heated to 80° C., when 2 c.c. of the air measured at 0° C. are found to have escaped. How much air was in the vessel before heating?

16. At what temperature, when under a pressure of 75 cm. of mercury, will 2 liters of gas measured at 46° C. and 76 cm. pressure measure 1.8 liters?

17. If a quantity of gas measured at 0° C. and 76 cm. pressure is subjected to a pressure of 775 mm., how much must the temperature be increased that the volume may remain the same?

18. If the temperature of a certain volume of air is increased from − 10° to 30° C., how much must the pressure be increased to keep the volume constant?

19. A certain volume of gas is enclosed in a vessel at 76 cm. pressure and − 20° C. It is then heated to 40° C. What is the pressure on the sides of the vessel measured in terms of atmospheres?

20. A volume of air at standard temperature and pressure is compressed to ⅙ its original volume and the temperature then raised to 25° C. What will now be the pressure in atmospheres?

21. A liter flask was filled with air at − 10° C. and 750 mm. pressure. If the barometer rises to 760 mm., to what temperature must the flask be raised to drive out ½ the air that was in it when it was filled?

22. To how many atmospheres pressure must a liter of gas measured at 76 cm. pressure and −20° C. be subjected to be condensed to ¼ a liter when the temperature is 40° C.?

23. A liter of hydrogen at 760 mm. pressure and 0° C. weighs .0896 g. What will 10 liters weigh at −20° C. and 750 mm. pressure?

24. If a liter of nitrogen at 0° C. and 76 cm. pressure weighs 1.25 g., how many liters at 25°. C. and 74 cm. pressure will be required to weigh 8 g.?

25. The sp. gr. of air at 20° C. normal pressure is .00118. What will be the weight of a liter of air at −20° C.?

26. A liter of chlorine gas at 0° C. and 76 cm. pressure weighs 3.17 g. If the pressure is decreased to 74 cm., what must the temperature be that a liter of gas may weigh 2 g.?

27. The air in a flexible rubber bag is found to occupy a volume of 1 cu. ft. at 30 in. pressure and 20° C. If the bag is plunged to a depth of 170 ft. in water, the temperature of which is 10° C., what will be its volume?

28. On the top of a mountain the barometer stands at 70 cm. and the temperature is 10° C., while in the valley the barometer stands at 758 mm. and the thermometer at 20° C. What are the relative densities of the air in the two places?

29. The gas enclosed in a piston tube is compressed to ¼ its original volume measured at 76 cm. pressure, and the temperature is raised from 10° to 100° C. What is the pressure on each sq. cm. of the piston?

30. A cylinder contains air at 5° C. and 4 atmospheres pressure. Show that if the air is heated to 565° C., the cylinder must be able to stand a pressure of over 12 atmospheres in order not to break.

31. A volume of gas in a graduated flask over water measures 750 c.c. The water in the flask stands 34 cm. above that outside, and the barometer stands at 745 mm. How much will this gas measure if exposed to standard pressure? The sp. gr. of mercury is 13.6.

32. How great a weight will a balloon containing 1000 liters of air at 40° C. raise on a day when the barometer reading is 760 mm. and the temperature 0° C.? The balloon itself weighs 100 g. and a liter of air at 0° C. and 760 mm. pressure weighs 1.293 g.

33. A cylinder 48 in. long and closed at one end is filled with air at 77° C. and 30 in. barometric pressure. If the cylinder is sunk open end down to a depth of 68 ft. in water, the temperature at this depth being 14° F., what will be the volume of the air as compared with that at the surface?

34. A tube 1 m. long, closed at one end and filled with air at 0° C. and 76 cm. pressure, is plunged open end down into a cistern of mercury at the same temperature. If the lower end of the tube is 75 cm. below the surface of the mercury in the cistern, what is the length of the air column in the tube?

MAGNETISM AND ELECTRICITY

1. Two small insulated spheres, one charged with 10 units of positive electricity and the other with 10 units of negative electricity, are placed at a distance of 12 cm. apart. How much is the attractive force between them?

2. If one of the spheres in the previous problem had been charged with 15 units of electricity, what would have been their mutual attraction?

3. How far apart must the spheres in the first problem be placed that their mutual attraction shall be $\frac{1}{4}$ dyne?

4. A small metallic sphere is charged with 10 units of electricity. On bringing another similar sphere to a distance of 20 cm. from it, the second sphere is found to be attracted with a force of 1 dyne. What is the charge upon the second sphere?

5. If the two spheres in the previous problem were made to touch each other and then placed at a distance of 4 cm. apart, what would be the mutual force exerted by them?

6. Two spheres charged one with + 20 and the other with − 15 units of electricity are placed at a certain distance apart. They are then brought into contact and afterward placed in their original position. What is the ratio of the forces acting between them before and after contact?

7. Two small spheres are charged with + 16 and − 4 units of electricity. With what force will they attract each other when at a distance of 4 cm.?

8. If the two spheres of the previous problem are made to touch and then returned to their former positions, with what force will they act on each other? Will this force be attraction or repulsion?

9. When two small metallic spheres are equally charged and placed 8 cm. apart, they are found to repel each other with a force of 2 dynes. How much is the charge on each sphere?

10. A magnetic pole of 80 units strength is 20 cm. distant from a similar pole of 30 units strength. Find the force between them.

11. A magnetic pole of 6 units strength is placed in a field of 0.25 unit strength. What is the force exerted on the pole?

12. A wire 10 ft. long has a diameter of 1 mm. What must be the diameter of a wire 40 ft. long to offer (*a*) the same resistance? (*b*) ¼ as much resistance?

13. What length of wire .25 mm. in diameter will have the same resistance as 50 m. of wire .75 mm. in diameter?

14. If the resistance of a wire 5 m. long and 1 mm. in diameter is 2.5 ohms, what will be the resistance of a wire 10 m. long and .5 mm. in diameter?

15. If the resistance of a wire 10 m. long and .5 mm. in diameter is 8 ohms, what length of the same kind of wire 1 mm. in diameter will be needed to give a resistance of .5 ohm?

16. A piece of wire 5 m. long and .75 mm. in diameter gives 40 ohms resistance. What must be the diameter of a 10 m. piece of wire of the same material in order that its resistance may be only 20 ohms?

17. What e. m. f. is necessary to maintain a current of 10 amperes through a resistance of 40 ohms?

18. If 4 rods of wire weighing 4 lbs. has a resistance of 5 ohms, what will be the resistance of a wire 5 yds. long which weighs 2 lbs.?

19. If 5 yds. of wire weighing 22 oz. has a resistance of 4.7 ohms, what will be the resistance of a wire 10 rods long which weighs 20 lbs?

20. If 100 ft. of wire weighing 5 lbs. has a resistance of .07 ohm, what will be the resistance of a mile of wire which weighs 100 lbs.?

21. If a mile of wire .15 cm. in diameter has a resistance of 2.5 ohms, what is the length of a wire of the same material .05 cm. in diameter which has the same resistance?

22. What are the relative resistances of two wires, one of which is 40 cm. long and weighs 50 g., and the other 25 cm. long and weighs 20 g.?

23. If an ohm is equal to the resistance of a column of mercury 106 cm. long and 1 sq. mm. in area of cross-section, what is the resistance of a column of mercury 3 m. long and 4 sq. mm. in area of cross-section?

24. If the conductivities of mercury and copper are as 1 to 50.7, what is the resistance of a copper wire 1 mile long and .35 in. in diameter?

25. If a piece of wire 10 m. long and .25 mm. in diameter offers a resistance of 3 ohms, what length of wire .5 mm. in diameter will be required to give 1.5 ohms resistance?

26. Two wires of the same length and material are found to have resistances of 6 and 10 ohms respectively. If the diameter of the first is .8 mm., what·is the diameter of the second?

27. If a mile of copper wire having a diameter of .13 in. has a resistance of 3.25 ohms, what must be the diameter of a copper wire 440 yds. long which has a resistance of 2 ohms?

28. A meter of hard-drawn pure copper wire which weighs .2125 g. offers a resistance of .69 of an ohm. If the resistance of a piece of wire 20 m. long, weighing 12.75 g., is 1.65 ohms, what is the conductivity of this wire as compared with pure copper wire?

29. An iron wire weighing .188 lb. per ft. and having a diameter of .27 in. was found to have a resistance of .004574 ohm per ft. What is its conductivity as compared with a similar piece of pure copper wire?

30. What is the diameter of a piece of pure copper wire, 100 miles of which offers a resistance of 120 ohms? Specific resistance of copper is 1.6.

31. If the resistance of a platinum wire 5 m. long and weighing 5 g. is 10 ohms, what is the resistance of platinum per c.c., its sp. gr. being 20.33?

32. If the specific resistances of zinc and platinum are to each other as 1 is to 2, and a piece of zinc wire 20 ft. long and 1 mm. in diameter has a certain resistance, how long a piece of platinum wire of diameter .3 mm. will have the same resistance?

33. A piece of zinc wire 1 ft. long has a certain resistance. What is the length of a piece of platinum wire of twice the diameter that has the same resistance?

34. The specific resistances of copper and iron are to each other as 1 to 6. How long a copper wire .2 mm. in diameter will have the same resistance as an iron wire 1000 ft. long and .5 mm. in diameter?

35. If the resistance of 1000 ft. of copper wire 2 mm. in diameter is 1.6 ohms, what will be the resistance of 4000 ft. of iron wire 5 mm. in diameter. The conductivity of iron is $\frac{1}{6}$ that of copper.

36. If the conductivities of iron and copper are as 1 to 6, and the diameters of the two wires, one of iron and the other of copper, are to each other as 3 to 2, what must be their relative lengths if they have the same resistance?

37. If the resistance of a centimeter cube of a certain metal is .125 ohm, what will be the resistance of a wire of this metal 3 m. long and 1 mm. in diameter?

38. The resistance of a wire 2 m. long and $\frac{1}{2}$ a mm. in diameter is 1 ohm. What is the resistance of two pieces of this kind of wire, each 10 m. long and 1 mm. in diameter, if joined in multiple arc?

39. Two pieces of wire have resistances of 75 and 120 ohms respectively. Find their joint resistance in multiple arc.

40. Three wires whose resistances are 10, 12, and 14 ohms respectively are joined in multiple arc. What is the joint resistance?

41. What is the joint resistance of five pieces of wire in multiple if each piece alone has a resistance of 2 ohms?

42. If the resistance between two points is 25 ohms, what must be the resistance of an additional wire connecting these two points in order to reduce the resistance to 20 ohms?

43. The resistance offered by a piece of wire is 200 ohms. If this piece of wire is drawn out to 4 times its original length, kept of uniform diameter, cut into four pieces of equal length, and these pieces joined in multiple, what will be the resistance?

44. Find the ratio between the resistances of two wires of the same material, one of which is 25 m. long and .15 mm. in diameter, and the other 15 m. long and .25 mm. in diameter.

45. If the resistance of iron per c.c. is 9.825 microhms, and of German silver per c.c. 21.17 microhms, what will be the resistance offered by an iron wire 30 cm. long and 1 mm. in diameter, and German silver wire 20 cm. long and 2 mm. in diameter, if joined in multiple arc?

46. What is the resistance of the two wires of the previous problem if joined in series?

47. If the specific resistance of copper is to that of iron as 1 to 6, how much iron wire 2.25 mm. in diameter will be required to give the same resistance as 25 m. of copper wire .5 mm. in diameter?

48. A piece of wire 10 m. long and .25 mm. in diameter offers a resistance of 6 ohms. A second piece, which is 10 m. long, .5 mm. in diameter, and of specific resistance 6 times that of the first, is joined in multiple. What is the joint resistance?

49. Two wires have resistances of .15 and .05 ohm per foot respectively. If the one having the higher resistance

is 10 ft. long, what must be the length of the other to make the resistance they offer when connected in multiple arc ¼ what it is when they are connected in series?

50. A battery of 10 cells is connected in series with an external resistance of 50 ohms. The e. m. f. of each cell is 1.25 volts and its internal resistance 2 ohms. What is the strength of the current?

51. A battery of 20 cells is connected in series with an external resistance of 40 ohms. If the e. m. f. of each cell is 1.1 volts, and its internal resistance 1.5 ohms, what is the strength of the current?

52. What current would be furnished in the previous problem if the cells were arranged, (*a*) 4 abreast and 5 in series ; (*b*) 5 abreast and 4 in series?

53. Six cells, each of e. m. f. 1 volt and internal resistance .75 ohm, are to be connected with an external resistance of 1 ohm. (*a*) Show by diagrams the possible methods of arrangement of the cells. (*b*) Prove by numerical work the best arrangement for a maximum current.

54. A current is to be sent through a wire 10 m. long and .25 mm. in diameter. The wire offers a resistance of 0.1 ohm per 3 linear ft. If 4 cells are employed, each of e. m. f. 1 volt and internal resistance 2 ohms, what is the best arrangement for maximum current?

55. Find the current strength through an external resistance of 10,000 ohms, when a battery of 50 cells, each of e. m. f. 1.25 volts and internal resistance of 2.5 ohms, is arranged for maximum

56. How would the current in Problem 54 be affected if the area of the battery plates were doubled?

57. Suppose it were possible to double the e. m. f. of each of the cells in Problem 54, how would this affect the current ?

58. If a cable offers a resistance of 10 ohms per mile, what will be the strength of a current which can be sent through 1000 miles of this cable by a battery of 100 cells, each having an e. m. f. of 1.5 volts and an internal resistance of 4 ohms?

59. Eight cells, each of e. m. f. 1 volt and internal resistance 1.5 ohms, are to be arranged for maximum current through an external resistance of 6 ohms. What is the arrangement of the cells?

60. A battery which generates a current of 5 amperes has its poles connected by 3 wires of the same material, but whose diameters are 0.5 mm., 0.6 mm., and 0.8 mm. What part of the current flows through each?

61. A battery having an e. m. f. of 8 volts has an internal resistance of 20 ohms. If the current it produces is sent through 5 wires, each having a resistance of 10 ohms, how many amperes current will go through each wire?

62. How many cells, each having an e. m. f. of 1.2 volts and an internal resistance of 4 ohms, will be required to send a current of .045 ampere through the larger of two wires arranged in multiple arc, one of which has a resistance of 600 ohms and the other of 400 ohms?

63. What would be the current sent through the wires in Problem 62, if the cells were arranged in multiple arc?

64. Three wires, each having a resistance of 15 ohms, were joined abreast and a current of 3 amperes sent through them. How much was the e. m. f. of the current?

65. Two wires, each having a resistance of 10 ohms, are arranged abreast and a current of 10 amperes is sent through them. What is the voltage of the current?

66. The e. m. f. of a certain battery is 10 volts and the strength of the current obtained through an external resistance of 4 ohms is 1.25 amperes. What is the internal resistance of the battery?

67. What is the greatest resistance through which 12 cells arranged in series, each having an e. m. f. of 1.5 volts and an internal resistance of .5 ohm, will send a current of 1.5 amperes?

68. A certain number of cells arranged abreast give a current of .145 ampere. The e. m. f. of each cell is 1.5 volts, the internal resistance 6 ohms, and the external resistance of the circuit 10 ohms. How many cells are there?

69. What is the arrangement for maximum current when a battery of 6 cells, each having an e. m. f. of 1 volt and an internal resistance of 4 ohms, is employed to send a current through an external resistance of 4 ohms?

70. What is the arrangement for strongest possible current when 18 cells, each having an e. m. f. of 1 volt and an internal resistance of 3 ohms, are employed to send a current through a wire which offers a resistance of 24 ohms?

71. If the external resistance of Problem 59 had been 35 ohms, what would have been the best arrangement?

72. If the cells in Problem 59 were to send a current through a resistance of 2 ohms, what would be the best arrangement?

73. How many cells, each of e. m. f. 1.5 volts and internal resistance 2 ohms, will be needed to send a current of at least 1 ampere through an external resistance of 40 ohms?

74. What is the greatest current obtainable from a battery of 10 cells connected with an external resistance of 20 ohms, if each cell has an e. m. f. of 1.5 volts and an internal resistance of 5 ohms?

75. What is the best arrangement of 12 cells, each of e. m. f. 1.25 volts and of internal resistance of 2 ohms, for an external resistance of 1000 ohms?

76. How can 24 cells, each having an e. m. f. of 1.8 volts and an internal resistance of 1.5 ohms, be best arranged to send a current through a resistance of 6 ohms?

77. How can 36 cells, each having an e. m. f. of 1.5 volts and an internal resistance of 3 ohms, be best arranged to send a current through an external resistance of 12 ohms?

78. What will be the current strength in Problems 75 and 76?

79. What arrangement of the cells in Problem 76 would send the strongest current through an external resistance of 25 ohms?

80. What would be the best arrangement for the cells in Problem 75 if the external resistance was ¾ of an ohm? How much would the current be?

81. How would you arrange 80 cells, each having an e. m. f. of 2 volts and an internal resistance of 4 ohms, so as to send the strongest possible current through a resistance of 12 ohms? How much will the current be?

82. What is the best arrangement for a battery of 64 cells if it is to send a current through a resistance of 2 ohms? The e. m. f. of each cell is 2 volts and the internal resistance 4 ohms.

83. A battery of 16 similar cells is found when grouped in series to give a voltage of 20. The internal resistance of each cell is 2.5 ohms. Find the strength of the greatest current that can be sent through a resistance of 10 ohms.

84. It is necessary to send a current of 2 amperes through a resistance of 30 ohms. Will a battery of 80 Bunsen cells, each having an e. m. f. of 1.36 volts and an internal resistance of .4 ohm, be able to do this?

85. The resistance of a battery is 3 ohms, and it produces a current of .5 ampere through an external resistance of 1.5 ohms. What is its e. m. f.?

86. What e. m. f. is needed to maintain a current of 4 amperes through a wire that offers a resistance of 5 ohms?

87. Twelve cells arranged 4 in series and 3 abreast, produce ½ an ampere current through an external resistance of 5 ohms. If the internal resistance of each cell is 3 ohms, what is the e. m. f.?

88. What is the e. m. f. of a cell which has an internal resistance of 2 ohms, if 16 of these cells, arranged 4 in series and 4 abreast, will produce a current of 3 amperes?

89. Ten cells arranged abreast, each having a resistance of 8 ohms, produce a current of .5 ampere through an external resistance of 2 ohms. What is the e. m. f. of each cell?

90. Two batteries, one of which has a resistance of 30 ohms and the other of 40 ohms, were successively joined in circuit with a galvanometer of no appreciable resistance and a resistance box. With a resistance of 50 ohms the first battery gave a deflection of 30°, but 300 ohms more were needed to cause the second battery to give the same deflection. What is the ratio of the e. m. f. of these batteries?

91. A battery was joined in simple circuit with a 10,000 ohm astatic galvanometer and a resistance box. When 10,000 ohms were placed in the circuit the needle was deflected 30°. Another battery connected with the same galvanometer required a resistance of 2500 ohms to cause the same deflection. Compare the e. m. f. of the two batteries.

92. How many lamps, each of resistance 20 ohms, and requiring a current of .8 ampere, can be lighted by a dynamo that has an output of 4000 watts?

93. How many lamps like those of Problem 92 can be lighted by a dynamo capable of doing two-horse power of external work?

94. How many lamps, arranged in multiple, can be lighted by a 440-volt dynamo, whose resistance is 4 ohms, if each lamp requires a current of 1.2 amperes and has a resistance of 20 ohms?

MISCELLANEOUS

1. A rifle weighing 5 lbs. discharges a 4-oz. bullet with a velocity of 100 ft. per second. What will be the velocity of the rifle in the opposite direction?

2. A ball weighing 150 g. and moving at the rate of 30 cm. per second strikes a ball at rest which weighs 400 g. If the smaller ball rebounds with a velocity of 10 cm. per second, what is the velocity of the larger ball after collision?

3. A ball weighing 40 lbs. and moving with a velocity of 30 ft. per second strikes a ball weighing 200 lbs. which is at rest. The smaller ball rebounds with a velocity of 8 ft. per second. What will be the velocity of the larger ball after collision?

4. A mass of 5 lbs., moving with a velocity of 20 ft. per second, meets fairly a body weighing 1 lb. and moving in the opposite direction with a velocity of 75 ft. per second. After collision the mass rebounds with a velocity of 3 ft. per second. What is the velocity of the body after collision?

5. A bullet weighing 2 oz. is shot into a body weighing 30 lbs. hanging freely suspended. If the velocity of the bullet is 1500 ft. per second, what will be the vertical height to which the body will be raised?

6. A wooden pendulum weighing 20 lbs. is struck by an ounce bullet and swung to a vertical height of 2 in. What was the velocity of the bullet at the instant of impact?

7. A wooden pendulum weighing 2 lbs. is struck by a bullet weighing 1 oz. and swung to a vertical height of 3 in. With what velocity did the pendulum begin to swing?

8. A Maxim gun delivers 300 1-oz. bullets per minute with a speed of 1600 ft. a second. What force is necessary to hold the gun still? [Lodge.]

9. Calculate the magnitude of the resultant of two forces, of 18 and 20 units respectively, acting from the same point and making with each other an angle of 120°.

10. If a rectangular mass of cork 20 × 4 × 8 cm. is counterpoised in air by 100 g. of metal, find the weight of the cork. Neglect lifting effect of air on metal.

11. Find the height of the homogeneous atmosphere when the mercury barometer reads 76 cm.

12. A barometer tube contains air above the mercury column. On a certain day the mercury stands at 25 in. when the space above it is 6 in. long, and at 24 in. when the space is made only 5 in. long by letting the tube lower down into its cistern. Find the true atmospheric pressure. [Lodge.]

13. A mass of air occupying 5 c.c. is allowed to enter the space above the mercury column in a barometer, and there expands until it occupies 15 c.c. The column of mercury is now 53.33 cm. high. How high was it before the air was allowed to enter?

14. A uniform door 4 ft. wide weighs 50 lbs. The two hinges are 8 ft. apart, and the load is equally divided between them. What is the horizontal pull on the upper hinge? the vertical pull? the resultant of these two? Show by diagram the magnitude and direction of this resultant.

15. What is the height of a mercury barometer when the atmospheric pressure is 1.1 megadynes per sq. cm.? the height of a water barometer?

16. A rectangular body, the volume of which is to be determined, is measured with a scale, the divisions of which are 0.8 their designated length. Will the computed volume be too large or too small? How much?

17. If the density of the body of Problem 16 is to be determined, will the computed value be too large or too small? How much?

18. A cubical box $12 \times 12 \times 12$ in. is $\frac{1}{3}$ full of mercury and $\frac{2}{3}$ full of water. Find the pressure on one of its sides.

19. How much hot water at 90° C. will be required to change 25 g. of ice at $-20°$ to water at 20°?

20. How much steam at 100° C. will melt 1000 g. of ice at $-10°$?

21. A cubical block of uniform density and 10 cm. on a side weighs 10 lbs. It is fastened to a vertical wall by a horizontal pin at the middle of the upper edge of one face of the cube. What is the force tending to pull the pin from the wall?

22. Weights of 7 and 3 lbs. are placed at the ends of a weightless rod and balanced on a pivot. How must the pivot be shifted when the weights are interchanged if equilibrium is still maintained?

23. A body suspended from the two arms of a false balance has apparent weights of 10 and $10\frac{1}{2}$ lbs. What is the ratio of the arms of the balance?

24. A uniform rod is bent into the form of an isosceles

triangle, the equal sides being 10 cm. long and the base 12 cm. long.   Find the center of gravity of the rod.

25. A man ascends a ladder leaning against a wall. Show by means of a diagram whether the ladder will be most likely to slip when the man is at the top or bottom.

26. A uniform rod 3 ft. long, hinged at one end, has a force of 10 lbs. acting vertically upward on the free end. Two ft. from the hinge is suspended a weight of 9 lbs.   If the force holds the rod in a horizontal position, what is the weight of the rod?

27. A steelyard formed from a uniform rod 40 in. long and weighing 10 lbs. has a sliding weight of 2 lbs.   If the fulcrum is 6 in. from one end, what is the greatest weight that can be weighed by the steelyard?

28. A body passed over 80 ft. in the first 4 seconds and 350 in the first 10 seconds.   What was its initial velocity and what its acceleration?

29. A body passes over 300 ft. in 5 seconds and has a final velocity of 100.   What was its initial velocity?

30. A spring balance is suspended by its ring; a second spring balance is attached to the first by its hook and in an inverted position.   The reading of the first balance is 3 lbs. 8 oz.; that of the second is 3 lbs.   What correction must be applied to the second balance when used in a horizontal position?   Is it an additive or subtractive correction?

31. The second spring balance of the last problem reads, in case of a certain horizontal pull, 9.25 lbs.   What is the true reading?

32. A spring balance is suspended by its ring; a second spring balance is attached to the first by its hook and in an inverted position.   The reading of the first spring balance is 3.5 lbs., that of the second 3 lbs.   The zero error of the

second balance in a vertical position is 0.25 lb. What is the correction for this balance when used in a horizontal position?

33. If the zero error of the second spring balance of Problem 32 were − 0.25 lb., what would be the correction to apply in case the balance be used in a horizontal position?

34. A square 1 ft. on a side has weights of 2, 4, 6, and 8 g. placed at the corners. Find the center of gravity of the weights.

35. Find the center of gravity of weights of 4, 18, 12, and 14 lbs. placed at the corners of a square 12 in. on a side.

36. A triangular piece of board is in the shape of an isosceles triangle, with its two equal sides 5 ft. long and its base 8 ft. long. A weight of 10 lbs. is hung at its vertex. The weight of the board is 10 lbs. Find the center of gravity of the whole.

37. A room has a volume of 150 cu. yds. The barometer rises from 28 to 30 in. Find how many cu. yds. of air in the room at the higher pressure have entered during the rise.

38. Two bodies start from the same point, one moving east with a uniform velocity of 4 ft. per second, and the other north with a uniform acceleration. If at the end of 5 seconds they are 25 ft. apart, what is the acceleration of the second body?

39. A body is shot up a frictionless plane rising 3 in 5 with a velocity of 60 ft. per second. How long before it will slide back to its starting place?

40. A body after sliding down a frictionless inclined plane rising 1 in 5 traverses 50 ft. on a frictionless horizontal plane in 4 seconds. What was the length of the inclined plane?

41. Two weights of 10 and 6 lbs. hang by a cord passing over a frictionless pulley. With what acceleration will the smaller weight rise?

42. A 1-lb. weight hangs over the edge of a smooth table and drags a 15-lb. mass along the surface. Find the acceleration and the tension in the string that joins the two masses.

43. What weight attached to a 6-lb. mass and hanging over the edge of a smooth table will move the mass 6 ft. along the table in 2 seconds?

44. An engine raises a 3-ton cage up a coalpit shaft at the uniform rate of 33 ft. per second. What is the tension in the rope?

45. If the cage of Problem 44 is raised with a uniform acceleration of 6 ft. per second per second, what is the tension in the rope? [Lodge.]

46. A man weighing 150 lbs. goes up and down in an elevator which rises and falls with an acceleration of 5 ft. per second per second. What is his pressure against the bottom of the elevator?

47. A U-tube standing vertically on a table has its arms filled with water to the height of 8 in. A volume of linseed oil of sp. gr. .94, sufficient to fill 8 in. of the tube, is now poured into one of the arms. At what height above the table will be the junction of the oil and water?

48. What weight of lead of sp. gr. 11 must be fastened to 5 lbs. of wood of sp. gr. .5, so that the whole shall weigh 10 lbs. in water?

49. At what depth in the sea will the pressure be double what it is at a depth of 10 ft., the barometer standing at 30 in.?

50. A gas bubble 1 in. in diameter is in water 60 ft. below the surface. What diameter will it have on reaching the surface? The barometer stands at 30 in.

51. On account of the air in the top of a barometer tube 32 in. long, the mercury column stands at 28.8 in. when the true reading is 29.1. What will be the true reading when this barometer indicates a pressure of 29 in.?

52. What will be the resulting temperature obtained by placing 500 g. of mercury of 0° C. in 200 g. of water at 60° C.?

53. A liter of air is measured at 0° C. and 760 mm. pressure. When the temperature is increased 100° C. and the pressure 240 mm., the volume is found to be 1038.39 c.c. What is the coefficient of expansion of air?

54. Five hundred g. of platinum are dropped into 100 g. of water at 16°.8 C., raising the temperature thereby to 20° C. What was the temperature of the platinum?

55. A ball of lead at 75° C. was dropped into 3 lbs. of water at 10° C. The resulting temperature was found to be 29° C. What was the weight of the ball?

56. How much heat is given out when 100 g. of mercury at 110° C. are frozen?

57. A ball is shot into the air with a velocity of 320 ft. per second, its path making an angle of 45° with the horizon. With what velocity must a second ball be shot vertically to rise to the same height?

58. A stone is dropped from a balloon ascending with a velocity of 16 ft. per second and reaches the ground in 15 seconds. How high was the balloon when the stone was dropped?

59. If a hole 1 ft. sq. is cut in the bottom of a ship 25 ft. below the surface of the water, what force must be exerted to keep the water out? Consider that a cu. ft. of sea-water weighs 64 lbs.

60. A stone is thrown vertically upward with a velocity that will cause it to rise 144 ft. Two seconds after, another stone is thrown from the same spot in the same direction and with the same velocity. How long after the second stone was thrown and how far above the starting place will the two collide?

61. A uniform rod 30 in. long lying on a smooth table projects 6 in. over the edge of the table. What part of the weight of the rod must a weight be, which, when placed at the extremity of the projecting end, will just cause the rod to tip from the table?

62. A square 1 ft. on a side has weights of 1, 2, 3, and 4 lbs. placed at each of its corners. At what distance from the center of the square is the center of gravity of the weights?

VALUE OF BROWN & SHARPE WIRE–GAUGE NUMBERS

Number.	Diameter mm	Number	Diameter mm
1	7.348	18	1.024
2	6.544	19	0.912
3	5.827	20	0.812
4	5.189	21	0.723
5	4.621	22	0.644
6	4.115	23	0.573
7	3.656	24	0 511
8	3.264	25	0 455
9	2.906	26	0.405
10	2.582	27	0.361
11	2.305	28	0.321
12	2.053	29	0.286
13	1.828	30	0.255
14	1.628	31	0.227
15	1.459	32	0.202
16	1.291	33	0.180
17	1.150		

SPECIFIC GRAVITIES

Alcohol	0.8	Lead	11 3
Brass	8.4	Linseed Oil	0 94
Cork	0.25	Mercury	13.6
Coal	1.8	Nickel	8.9
Copper	8.9	Nitric Acid	1.56
Copper Sulphate Solution	1.2	Oak Wood	0.85
Ether	0.73	Platinum	21.5
Glass (flint)	3.5	Silver	10 5
Gold	19 3	Sulphuric Acid	1.84
Hydrochloric Acid	1.22	Tin	7.3
Iron	7.8	Oil of Turpentine	0.87
Kerosene	0.8	Zinc	7.1

Weight of 1 cu. ft. of water approximately 62.5 lbs.

Name	Coefficient of Expansion Cubical	Melting Point Centigrade	Boiling Point Centigrade	Specific Heat	Latent Heat of Melting Gm. Deg. C	Latent Heat of Vaporization Gm. Deg. C
Alcohol	.00106		78 2	.65		206
Aluminum	.000070	700		212		
Brass	.000057	1100		.094		
Copper	.000051	1100		.093		
Glass	.000025			.19		
Gold	.000044	1100		.032		
Ice				.5	80	536 (water)
Iron	.000036	1200		.11		
Lead	.000088	330		032		
Mercury	.000182	39	357	033	2.8	
Nickel	.000038	1500		.109		
Platinum	.000027	1900		.032		
Silver	.000058	1000		056	21	
Steam				5*		
Steel	.000034	1400		.17		
Sulphur	.0003	114	448	055	94	362
Tin	.000069	230	1500	.5	14	70
Turpentine		-10	160	.5		
Zinc	000088	420	1000	093	28	

* Pressure constant.

MATHEMATICAL FORMULÆ

The square of the hypotenuse of a right triangle = the sum of the squares of the legs.

The area of a triangle = $\frac{1}{2}$ the product of its base and altitude.

The circumference of a circle = π D or $2\,\pi$ R.

The area of a circle = $\dfrac{\pi D^2}{4}$ or πR^2.

The area of the surface of a sphere = πD^2 or $4\pi R^2$.

The volume of a sphere = $\dfrac{\pi D^3}{6}$ or $\dfrac{4\pi R^3}{3}$.

The volume of a prism or cylinder = area of base by altitude.

The volume of a pyramid or cone = area of base by $\frac{1}{3}$ the altitude.

EQUIVALENTS IN THE ENGLISH AND METRIC SYSTEMS

1 meter	= 39.37 inches.
1 inch	= 2.54 centimeters.
1 liter	= 1.056 quarts.
1 gram	= .035 ounce.
1 kilogram	= 2.2 pounds avoirdupois.
1 ounce	= 28.35 grams.
1 pound avoirdupois	= .4536 kilogram.

HARVARD COLLEGE

ADMISSION EXAMINATIONS
IN PHYSICS

1890–1900

PHYSICAL SCIENCE

[Omit any three questions. If the candidate answers more than five questions he should designate those which he wishes to have regarded as extra ones, otherwise his mark will be five times the *average* of the marks on the questions answered. Show the processes by which numerical answers are obtained.]

1. A certain body appears by the indications of a spring balance to weigh 15 g. in air and 10 g. in water.

(*a*) If the balance is correct, what is the specific gravity of the body?

(*b*) If each reading of the balance is only $\frac{8}{10}$ as large as it should be, what is the specific gravity of the body?

2. If the weight of a c.c. of air is .0012 g. at atmospheric pressure, how many times the ordinary atmospheric pressure would be required to compress air to the density of water, provided the law of compression should hold which your experiments have taught you?

3. Three forces, all applied to the same point, are in equilibrium with each other. If one of these is a force pulling north and another is a force pulling east, show how to find by means of a diagram the direction and magnitude of the third force. Mark the direction of each of the three forces in your figure by means of an arrowhead.

4. A uniform bar 6 ft. long and weighing 8 lbs. is loaded at one end with an 8-lb. weight

(*a*) At what distance from this end must a supporting point be placed in order that the whole may balance with the bar in a horizontal position?

(*b*) If the bar is hinged at the unloaded end, how much work must be done in order to raise the loaded end 2 ft.?

5. Describe, with a drawing, the apparatus which you have used in measuring the expansion of a metal bar.

6. Describe any experiment in sound upon which you have spent not less than one hour.

7. In a photographic camera using a single lens let the plate be so placed that the center only of the picture is distinct. Must the plate be pushed nearer the lens or pulled farther away in order that the edges of the picture may become distinct?

8. Let a coil of wire be placed with its plane vertical and extending east and west, and let a current of electricity be flowing in the coil in such a direction that in the top of the coil its course is from east to west. Draw a diagram showing the lines of magnetic force in a horizontal plane cutting through the middle of the coil. Mark each line with arrowheads at several points to indicate the direction of pointing of the magnetic needle at these points. [No more lines need be drawn than the student has himself observed in his laboratory work.]

Admission. (1) 1890.

PHYSICAL SCIENCE

ALTERNATIVE II

[Omit any three questions. Show the processes by which numerical answers are obtained.]

1. A rectangular-sided block of wood 10 cm. thick floats in water with 6 cm. of its depth submerged. Find specific gravity of block. Show your process of reasoning.

2. In determining the specific gravity of air by weighing a bottle, (a) when filled with air, (b) when empty, why is it important to have the inside of the bottle dry?

3. A door 8 ft. tall, 3 ft. wide, and weighing 50 lbs. is attached to a wall by one edge in an upright position at two points — the first 1 ft. above the bottom, the other 1 ft. below the top.

(a) How great is the total downward pull upon the wall at

each point?   (*b*) How great is the horizontal force exerted on the wall at each point, and is this force a push or a pull?

4. A ball weighing 20 g. moving with a velocity of 50 cm. per second strikes centrally a ball weighing 100 g. which is at rest. After the collision the larger ball moves north with a velocity of 12 cm. per second.   What velocity has the smaller ball after the collision, and in what direction is it moving?

5. A volume of air at 27° C. and under a pressure of 75 cm. of mercury contains 1000 c.c.   What would be its volume at 127° C. under a pressure of 150 cm. of mercury?

6. Describe carefully the process you would follow in finding the dew-point, and show why the dew-point is important for weather predictions.

7. Draw a diagram illustrating the use of a lens for throwing upon a screen the image of an object.   Mark the principal focus of the lens and show how to find the position and size of the object.

8. With a two-fluid galvanic cell, using zinc and copper plates, is the current supposed to go from zinc to copper, or from copper to zinc, inside the cell? outside the cell?   Does the zinc plate grow lighter or heavier while the current flows?   Does the copper plate grow lighter or heavier?   If a magnetic needle is placed just beneath a straight wire carrying a current from south to north, in what direction will the needle point?

Admission. (1) 1891.

PHYSICAL SCIENCE

ALTERNATIVE II : EXPERIMENTAL PHYSICS

[Omit any three questions. If the candidate answers more than five questions, he should indicate which ones he wishes to be considered as *extra* ones. Indicate the numerical processes by which answers are obtained.]

1. The deflections of different rods of the same material under equal loads are *proportional to the cubes of their lengths and inversely proportional to their widths and the cubes of their depths.*

If a rod 100 cm. long, 2 cm. broad, and 3 cm. thick is deflected 0.5 cm. when placed horizontal and loaded at the middle with a certain weight, what would be the deflection, under the same load, of a rod 50 cm. long, 2 cm. broad, and 1 cm. thick?

2. A cubical vessel, each side of which is 10 cm. square, has a tube 1 sq. cm. in cross-section and 20 cm. tall rising from the middle of its top. The tube is open at both ends, and both vessel and tube are full of water. Neglecting atmospheric pressure and weight of vessel and tube, find

(*a*) How great is the total pressure which the vessel as now filled exerts upon its support.

(*b*) How great is the total pressure exerted against the bottom of the vessel by the water within it.

If these pressures are not equal, explain the difference.

3. A cork of specific gravity .25, the volume of which is 10 c.c., floats upon mercury of specific gravity 13 6. How great is the volume of the submerged part of the cork?

4. A door 10 ft. tall, 5 ft. wide, and weighing 100 lbs. is attached to a wall by one edge in an upright position at two *points* — the first 1 ft. above the bottom, the other 1 ft below the top.

(*a*) How great is the total *downward* pull upon the wall at the two supporting points?

(*b*) How great is the *horizontal* force exerted upon the wall at each point, and is this force a push or a pull?

5. The coefficient of linear expansion of steel being .000012, what is the length at 0° C. of a bar which is just 1 m. long at 20° C.?

6. Describe carefully any process which you would recommend for determining the rate of vibration of a tuning fork.

7. The image of a clock-face is thrown upon a screen. The time is 12.30. Make a drawing of the *image* as seen by an observer looking from the lens.

8. A galvanic cell such as you have used is employed to send a current of electricity through 1 m. of No. 30 German-silver wire, and a perfectly similar cell to send a current through 2 m. of the same

kind of wire. Tell why the strengths of the two currents would not be exactly as 2 to 1.

If 50 m. of the wire were substituted for the 1 m., and 100 m. for the 2 m., would the strengths of the currents be more nearly as 2 to 1 ? Explain.

Admission. (1) 1892.

PHYSICAL SCIENCE

ALTERNATIVE II : EXPERIMENTAL PHYSICS

[Omit any three questions   Indicate the processes by which numerical answers are obtained.]

1. A certain beam 4 ft. long, placed horizontal and supported at the ends, is bent downward 0 5 in. by a load placed at the middle. How far would it be bent by the same load if it were 8 ft. long?

2. A vessel is filled with water to a depth of 40 cm. A cylinder of wood 30 cm. long and 100 sq. cm. in area of cross-section, the specific gravity of which is .05, extends upward through a hole in the bottom of the vessel, the top of the cylinder being 20 cm. beneath the surface of the water. Show whether the cylinder tends to rise or to fall and how great a force is required to hold it in its present position.

3. From the following data find the specific gravity of sulphuric acid :

Weight of bottle empty . . . . 50 g.
Weight of bottle filled with water   .   . . 150 g.
Weight of bottle filled with sulphuric acid   . . . 234 g.

How much would this result have been changed if 1 c.c. of the bottle had been left empty when it was weighed with water?

4. A uniform lever 6 ft. long and weighing 20 lbs. lies horizontally across a fulcrum 2 ft. from one end. A mass of 100 lbs. is suspended from the end of the short arm of the lever. How great must be the force applied at the end of the other arm in order that there may be equilibrium?

5. From the following data find the temperature after mixing :

Weight of water used . . . . 100 g.
Weight of mercury used . . . . 1000 g.
Original temperature of water . . . . 10°
Original temperature of mercury . . . . 100°
Specific heat of mercury . . . . .0333°
Number of heat units absorbed by the calorimeter . 80

6. Describe and explain the phenomena seen in boiling water, showing why the temperature of boiling depends upon the pressure.

7. Describe carefully the process by which you have found the shape and size of a real image formed by a lens.

8. Given 8 galvanic cells, each having an electromotive force of 1 volt and a resistance of 2 ohms, with an external resistance of 20 ohms, what will be the strength of the current when the cells are arranged in *series*, that is, with the zinc of one cell joined to the copper of the next? When in *multiple arc*, that is, with the zincs joined as one and the coppers joined as one?

Admission. (1) 1893

PHYSICAL SCIENCE

ALTERNATIVE II: EXPERIMENTAL PHYSICS

[Omit any three questions. In numerical questions indicate the process by which the answers are obtained.]

1. A pump is used to draw water from a well through a vertical pipe. How long may the pipe be, the barometer reading 76 cm. and the specific gravity of mercury being 13.6? Tell and explain what would happen if a small hole were bored in the wall of this pipe, when full of water, at a point halfway up.

2. A body weighs 50 g. alone in air. It is then tied to a piece of lead which weighs 100 g. alone in water, and the two together weigh 120 g. in water. What is the specific gravity of the body?

3. Define *work*.

A body weighing 100 lbs. rests upon an incline such that the body must move 10 ft. along the incline in order to *rise* 8 ft. How much work is required to draw the body 30 ft. along the incline when there is no friction? How much work is required to draw it the same distance when the coefficient of friction is $\frac{1}{4}$?

4. From the following data find the coefficient of expansion of a gas :

Vol. at 0° C. . .   . 200 c c.
Vol. at 1000 C. . . . . 275 c.c.
Pressure (by mercury gauge) 76 cm. throughout the experiment.

5. What temperature on the Centigrade scale corresponds to − 20° Fahrenheit?

6. Describe what you consider the best work requiring measurements that you have done in sound.

7. The focal length of a certain lens is 20 cm. An arrow 4 cm. long is placed 60 cm. from this lens, its direction being at right angles with the line drawn from it to the lens. What is the length of the image measured straight from tail to tip?

8. What is the object of amalgamating the zinc of a galvanic battery? State and explain the main advantage which two-fluid galvanic cells possess over single-fluid cells.

Admission. (1) 1894.

PHYSICAL SCIENCE

ALTERNATIVE II: EXPERIMENTAL PHYSICS

[Answer any five questions. In numerical questions indicate the process by which the answers are obtained.]

1. A cube of iron, each edge of which is 10 cm. long, floats upright in mercury. The density of the iron is 7.5, that of the mercury is 13.5. How high does the top of the cube float above the surface of the mercury?

2. A hole 1 sq. cm. in area of cross-section is opened in the wall of a water reservoir 30 m. below the water surface. A person undertakes to prevent leakage by covering the hole with his thumb. How great is the force required?

3. A uniform bar 10 ft. long leans with one end against a vertical wall at an angle of 45°; the other end rests upon the ground. The bar weighs 20 lbs. There is no friction between the bar and the wall, so that the force there exerted is entirely horizontal. How great is this force?

Illustrate the reasoning by means of a diagram.

4. If the rails of a car track vary 60° C. in temperature in the course of a year, and if their least length is 10 m., how much does the gap between the ends of two rails vary during the year, the coefficient of expansion being .000013?

5. If 1 g. of coal in burning gives out 7000 units of heat, and if the latent heat of melting for water is 80, how many grams of ice, taken at 0°, may be melted and raised to 20° C. by burning 1 g. of coal?

6. Describe "beats" of musical sounds. How and with what apparatus may they be produced?

7. Two plane mirrors are placed parallel, facing each other, and 2 ft. apart. A candle is placed halfway between them. Show by means of a diagram the position of the first three images seen in each mirror. Tell the distance of each of these images from the nearer mirror, and state the method by which you have determined these distances. [The course of the rays of light need not be shown in the diagram.]

8. Galvanic cell A has an electromotive force of 2 volts and a resistance of 6 ohms. Cell B has an electromotive force of 1 volt and a resistance of 3 ohms. How strong a current will each cell, used alone, send through a wire so short that its resistance may be neglected?

How strong will the current be if the two cells are joined in series, both working in the same direction?

Which cell will prevail, and how strong will be the current, if the two cells are joined in such a way as to oppose each other? [The electromotive forces and resistances would be likely to change in the course of such experiments But this fact is to be disregarded.]

Admission. (1) 1895

PHYSICAL SCIENCE

ALTERNATIVE II: EXPERIMENTAL PHYSICS

[Omit three questions.]

1. In a hydraulic (or hydrostatic) press the area of the small piston face is 1 sq. in. and that of the large piston face is 50 sq. in.

(a) If a force of 50 lbs. is applied to the small piston, how great is the force exerted upon the large piston, provided there be no friction?

(b) How much *work* is done upon the small piston while it moves 6 in., and how much is done at the same time upon the large piston? Name the unit in which the work is reckoned.

2. (a) Mention two of the most dense and two of the least dense solids that you know of.

(b) A cu. ft. of water weighs 62.4 lbs. A certain block of wood floats in water with ¼ of its volume above the surface. What is the *density* of this body in the foot-pound system?

3. A cord is fastened at each end, and a weight is suspended from it at a certain point where the cord bends at a right angle. The pull exerted at one end of the cord is 3 lbs. and at the other end 4 lbs. How heavy is the suspended weight? [The weight of the cord is neglected.]

4. Describe your laboratory experiments upon the collision of ivory balls, and state the general law to which you were led by means of them.

5. (a) Define the *dew-point*. At what time of the year and in what kind of weather is the dew-point very high? Under what conditions is it especially low?

(b) What is meant by the phrase, the *mechanical equivalent of heat*?

6. The velocity of sound being 340 m. per second, how long should a tube closed at one end be, in order that its resonance

may reinforce the sound from a tuning fork making 440 complete, that is, double, vibrations per second?

7. An object is placed near a double convex lens and then is moved outward from the lens along the principal axis until it passes far beyond the principal focus. Illustrate by means of a diagram the successive changes in position of the image caused by the movement of the object, showing the position of the principal axis and the principal focus, and marking several positions of the object as O_1, O_2, etc., and the corresponding images by I_1, I_2, etc.

8. (*a*) Trace the lines of magnetic force in the neighborhood of a galvanometer coil in which a current of electricity is flowing from south to north above and from north to south below, taking into account the earth's magnetic force, and showing the resultant effect of combining these with the force due to the current.

(*b*) A certain galvanic battery sends a very weak current through a small external resistance. What experiments could you make to determine whether the weakness of the current is due to very small electromotive force or to any large internal resistance in the battery?

Admission (1) 1896.

PHYSICAL SCIENCE

ALTERNATIVE II: EXPERIMENTAL PHYSICS

[Omit any five questions.]

1. The law for the stiffness of a beam is:

$$Stiffness\ is\ proportional\ to\ \frac{(width) \times (thickness)^3}{(length)^3}.$$

If a beam 10 ft. long, 2 in. through in one direction and 4 in. through in the other direction, bends 1 in. under a force of 500 lbs. applied parallel to its 4-in. dimension, how far would it bend under the same force applied parallel to its 2-in. dimension?

2. A water tank 8 ft deep, standing some distance above the

ground, closed everywhere except at the top, is to be emptied. The only means of emptying it is a flexible tube.

(*a*) What is the most convenient way of using the tube and how could it be set into operation?

(*b*) How long must the tube be to empty the tank completely?

3. A certain body weighing 150 lbs. will just float in sea-water of specific gravity 1.026. How great is the force, in addition to the buoyant force of the water, that would keep this body from sinking in fresh water?

4. A ladder 10 ft. long and weighing 20 lbs. leans against a vertical wall at an angle of 45°. The center of gravity of the ladder is at the center of its length. The wall is smooth, so that the force exerted where the ladder touches it is horizontal. Resolve the force exerted at the other end of the ladder into two forces, one vertical and one horizontal, and show how great each is.

[*Suggestion:* Make use in this problem of your knowledge of the moments of couples]

5. A mass of 2 lbs, moving with a velocity of 25 ft. per second, meets squarely a ball weighing 4 oz., moving in the opposite direction with a velocity of 80 ft. per second. After the collision the mass rebounds with a velocity of 2 ft. per second. What velocity has the ball just after the collision?

6. (*a*) Show how a thermometer may be constructed without use of any liquid

(*b*) Name, if you can, any liquids that boil at a lower temperature than water ; any that boil at a higher temperature than water.

7. How many inches of rainfall at a temperature of 10° C. would be sufficient to melt a layer of snow 1 ft. thick, of specific gravity o 2, taken at o° C. ?

("An inch of rainfall" means enough rain to make a layer of water 1 in. thick over the whole region of fall)

8. Describe carefully some method which you have used for measuring the velocity of sound.

9. (*a*) Define the *principal focus* of a lens.

(*b*) In what position with respect to this point is the object placed in the use of a simple magnifying glass?

(*c*) In what position with respect to the principal focus of the object-glass is the object placed in the use of a microscope?

10. A battery consisting of 3 cells in series, each having an electromotive force of 1 volt and an internal resistance of 2 ohms, is joined in circuit with another battery consisting of 3 cells in series, each having an electromotive force of 2 volts and an internal resistance of 1 ohm. In connecting the two *batteries*, like poles are joined together. There is no external resistance. How strong will the current through the circuit be?

Admission. (1) 1897.

BOTH METHODS

EXPERIMENTAL PHYSICS

[Omit any three questions]

1. How could you find the volume of an irregular lump of coal?

2. A ladder 20 ft. long and weighing 30 lbs., its center of gravity being at its middle point, stands upon the ground and leans at an angle of 45° against a smooth vertical wall. In this case the force exerted by the wall against the ladder is horizontal. How great is it?

[*Suggestion:* Calculate the moments with respect to the point where the ladder touches the ground.]

3. Explain with a diagram the principle of the reservoir of a student lamp.

4. Give reasons for believing that sound is a wave motion of the air or of some other medium transmitting it

5. Describe and explain a good method of freeing a ground-glass stopper which sticks hard in the mouth of a glass bottle.

Describe with a diagram and explain the device used in the balance of a watch to prevent the rate of the watch from changing with change of temperature.

6. If the latent heat of melting of ice is 80, how many g. of ice at 0° must be put into 1000 g. of water at 30° C. in order that the final temperature of the whole may be 10° C. ?

7. Represent a concave mirror by means of the arc of a circle drawn on your paper. Mark the position of the center of curvature and of the principal focus Draw the principal axis, and mark on it the position of a point the image of which would lie outside the center of curvature. Mark another point the image of which would be virtual.

8. A galvanic battery consists of 12 cells, each having an electromotive force of 2 volts and a resistance of 1 ohm. How great a current will this battery send through an external resistance of 20 ohms, if the cells are arranged in two sets of 6 cells each in series, and these two sets are joined together in multiple ?

Admission. (1) 1898.

BOTH METHODS

EXPERIMENTAL PHYSICS

[Candidates must hand in their notebooks at the time of the laboratory examination. Answer six questions]

1. A block of wood having a volume of 200 c.c. and a specific gravity 0.5 is used as a float to support a ball of lead that weighs 50 g. when under water. How much of the block will be beneath the surface of the water, the lead being attached to its under surface?

2. A cylindrical tube open at both ends is pushed down vertically into mercury until only 10 cm. of its length remains above the surface. This end is then closed air-tight, and the tube is raised until the air confined in its top has expanded to 30 cm. What is the difference in level of the surface of the mercury

inside and outside of the tube, the barometric pressure at the time being 75 cm. of mercury?

3. Two forces, one of 20 lbs. acting north, the other of 10 lbs. acting west, are applied at one point of a body. Two other forces, one acting south and the other acting east, are set to balance the first two, the point of application of the second pair being different from that of the first pair. Make a diagram to scale, showing how the whole may be arranged, and state the magnitude of each of the second pair of forces.

4. Make a diagram of a converging lens, drawing the principal axis and marking with a letter P the principal focus. Mark with an A the position of an object the image of which, as formed by the lens, will be real. Mark with a B the position of an object the image of which will be virtual. Will the image of the object at A be upright or inverted? larger than the object or smaller? Will the image of the object at B be upright or inverted? larger than the object or smaller?

5. If 200 g. of a metal of specific heat 0.1 are dropped into 50 g. of a liquid of specific heat 0.8, the metal being at 100° and the liquid at 20°, what will be the resulting temperature of the mixture?

6. If the weight of air in a chimney 10 m. tall and 0.2 sq. m. in cross-section is 2.58 kg., when the temperature of the air is 20° C., how great is the weight of air in the same chimney when the temperature of the air is 100° C.?

7. Describe briefly the voltameter method and the galvanometer method of measuring an electric current.

8. Define an *induced current of electricity* and describe the construction of some practical machine or piece of apparatus in which an induced current is generated.

9. Make a diagram showing an electric door-bell system, with one battery arranged to work two bells independently whenever the proper knobs are pushed.

Admission. (1) . 1899.

BOTH METHODS

EXPERIMENTAL PHYSICS

[Omit four of the following questions]

1. Air is forced into a bicycle tire by means of a pump 4 sq. cm. in cross-section (inside) and having a stroke 15 cm. long. The tire is at first entirely empty, but at last contains 600 c.c. of air at a pressure five times as great as the atmospheric pressure. How many strokes of the pump, working perfectly, have been needed to produce this result?

2. A body weighing 60 lbs. rests on an incline, the length of which is 10 ft., the height 6 ft., and the horizontal base 8 ft.

(*a*) How great a force parallel to the incline is required to keep the body moving up the incline with a uniform velocity, there being no friction?

(*b*) The pressure of the body against the incline is 48 lbs. If the coefficient of friction is 0.2, how great is the force required to draw the body with uniform velocity up the incline?

3. Define the dyne and the erg. A force of 15 dynes acting for 8 seconds imparts to a certain free body a final velocity of 10 cm. per second.

(*a*) How great is the mass of the body?

(*b*) How much work does the force do on the body in giving it the velocity mentioned?

4. Define *radiant energy* and *spectrum analysis*. Mention any example in which spectrum analysis has been used.

5. If the mechanical equivalent of heat, on the basis of pounds, feet, and degrees Centigrade is 1400, how far must a body, the specific heat of which is 0 2, fall in order that the heat generated by its fall may be great enough to raise the temperature of the body 6° C.?

6. Tell the vibration frequency of the notes E and G in the gamut which begins with 128 vibrations for the lower C.

7. What sort of eyeglasses should *near-sighted*, or short-sighted, persons wear? Illustrate your answer by means of a diagram.

8. A candle flame is 6 ft. from a wall ; a lens is between the flame and the wall, 5 ft. from the latter. A distinct image of the flame is formed on the wall.

(*a*) In what other position may the lens be placed, that a distinct image may be formed on the wall?

(*b*) How will the lengths of the two images compare, and which will be the longer?

9. Define the following terms relating to dynamos or electric motors : *armature, series wound, shunt wound.*

10. How strong a current will a cell having an electromotive force of 2 volts and an internal resistance of $\frac{1}{3}$ ohm send through an external circuit consisting of a 1-ohm resistance and a 2-ohm resistance joined in multiple (or parallel) circuit?

June, 1900.